WITHDRAWAL

THE TECHNICAL INSTITUTE IN AMERICA

THE CARNEGIE SERIES IN AMERICAN EDUCATION

The books in this series have resulted from studies supported by grants of the Carnegie Corporation of New York, and are published by McGraw-Hill in recognition of their importance to the future of American education.

The Corporation, a philanthropic foundation established in 1911 by Andrew Carnegie for the advancement and diffusion of knowledge and understanding, has a continuing interest in the improvement of American education. It financed the studies in this series to provide facts and recommendations which would be useful to all those who make or influence the decisions which shape American educational policies and institutions.

The statements made and views expressed in these books are solely the responsibility of the authors.

Books Published

Conant · The American High School Today
Glenny · Autonomy of Public Colleges
Henninger · The Technical Institute in America
Pierson · The Education of American Businessmen

In Preparation

Clark · Constraint in College Organization
Medsker · The Junior College

The Technical Institute in America

G. ROSS HENNINGER

Director, ASEE National Survey of Technical Institute Education;
President, Ohio College of Applied Science and Ohio Mechanics
Institute

McGraw-Hill Book Company, Inc.

NEW YORK   TORONTO   LONDON   1959

THE TECHNICAL INSTITUTE IN AMERICA

II

28240

Preface

A NEED exists in our post-secondary scheme of education for a large number of technical schools giving a more intensive and practical training than that now provided by the engineering colleges." With this opening statement, the report of the 1928–1929 study of technical institutes made by William E. Wickenden and Robert H. Spahr for the Society for the Promotion of Engineering Education (now the American Society for Engineering Education) was published.

The purpose of this 1959 report is to present the results of a national survey made in 1957–1958 for the purpose of bridging the intervening thirty years and revealing the present status and potential of technical institute education in America. Interestingly, the current findings are essentially identical with the earlier ones and could be expressed in the same words. There are significant supplementary findings, however, and these are presented in the ten chapters of this book.

This report is a compilation of facts and opinions about the educational and employment practices relating to the engineering technician as the demand for technological manpower has grown. It does not attempt to establish new objectives or educational goals, but it does indicate the potential of the technical institute idea in education by depicting accumulated experiences and present trends.

Although responsibility both for the operation of

the Survey and for the compilation of its results into this Report was vested in the Survey Director, the project represents the selfless labors of many people and the generous cooperation of many educational and business enterprises. Thus, the structure of the Survey project is the foundation of its scope and validity. The Survey Study Committee was established in 1954 by the Technical Institute Division of the American Society for Engineering Education and was authorized by the Society's General Council in 1955. The committee was responsible for the general development of the project and the dissemination of its results. The members are: Edward E. Booher, *Chairman*, Executive Vice President, McGraw-Hill Book Company, Inc.; G. Ross Henninger, President, Ohio College of Applied Science; Kenneth L. Holderman, Coordinator of Commonwealth Campuses, The Pennsylvania State University; Leo F. Smith, Dean of Instruction, Rochester Institute of Technology; and Karl O. Werwath, President, Milwaukee School of Engineering. The Survey Project Committee was organized in 1956 by the Study Committee and charged with direct responsibility for the development of Survey procedures and the general conduct of the project. Its members are: Kenneth L. Holderman, *Chairman;* H. Russell Beatty, President, Wentworth Institute; Maynard M. Boring, Consultant (Retired), Engineering Manpower, General Electric Company; C. J. Freund, Dean of Engineering, University of Detroit; George A. Gullette, Head, Department of Social Studies, North Carolina State College; Robert L. Shurter, Director, Humanities and Social Division, Case Institute of Technology; and Leo F. Smith.

The 143 volunteers from industry and education who constituted the fourteen Regional Committees provided the working structure for the field program. These people devoted a total of 753 man-days and traveled 125,182 man-miles to visit 96 educational institutions in 39 states and 140 industrial enterprises or other employers of technological personnel in 25 states. These visitations also included schools and institutes in the State of Nuevo León, Mexico, and the Province of Ontario, Canada. (See Appendix 1 for full listings.) Grateful acknowledgment is made hereby to the persons and enterprises whose cooperation made this project possible.

Especial acknowledgment is due to Bonham Campbell, Associate Professor of Engineering, University of California, Los Angeles, for six weeks of full-time service in Cincinnati collaborating in the analysis of data and the preparation of the manuscript of this Report, and to the University of California for making his time available for this and other Survey assignments; to Kenneth S. Oleson, Assistant Professor, Engineering Extension, Iowa State College, and later Director of Relations with Industry, Ohio College of Applied Science, for similar collaboration over a period of many months; to Iowa State College for the provision of office facilities and services to June, 1958, and to Ohio Mechanics Institute and Ohio College of Applied Science for furnishing these since June, 1958.

Acknowledgment is also due to many others who participated directly or indirectly, including the secretaries and typists who devoted many overtime hours to the processing of hundreds of pages of manuscript, and especially by the thirty-five members of the Survey's national and regional committees who read each of the ten chapters and contributed many valuable improvements to the final editing.

G. ROSS HENNINGER

Contents

The demand—the ratio of engineering technicians to engineers. The demand—numbers of engineering technicians. The demand—significance. Engineering technicians and engineers on the job. Follow-up of graduates in employment. Opportunities for women. Employment areas. Salary and advancement potential. What of the future?

10 Problems and Potentialities of the Technical Institute   149

Problems. Educational status. Professional status. Confusion in terminology. The "transfer credit" question. Trend in accreditation. Liaison with industry. Other problems. Potentialities of the technical institute. Educational aspect. Institutional aspect. Summary.

Appendixes

CHAPTER 1

The Technical Institute
in Higher Education[1]

EDUCATIONAL INSTITUTIONS, regardless of the time in history when they exist, tend to be a product of the social, political, economic, and technological forces impinging upon them. In the history of the United States this has been true from the earliest beginnings to the present.

Evolution of technical education in the United States

During the colonial period a majority of the population lived on farms, and such knowledges and skills as were needed there were passed down from father to son. The few skilled craftsmen of the day generally received their training through the serving of an apprenticeship. Preparation for the learned professions of the law, medicine, and the ministry was provided by a few church-supported colleges and universities located along the eastern seaboard.

[1] The term "technical institute" is used throughout this report, except where specifically indicated otherwise, to include all types of collegiate institutions and divisions of multipurpose collegiate institutions which offer programs in technical institute education.

1

With the opening of the Erie Canal and the growth of the urban population following the industrial revolution, a series of "Mechanics Institutes" were founded in the 1820s in several of the larger cities. These were designed to improve the welfare and education of the workingman —the craftsman and the artisan—through the "promotion of the useful arts" and the cultural and vocational development of their members. As the frontier moved westward a need was created for men with ability to locate and supervise the construction of railroads. Other developments of an increasingly technical nature also were giving rise to increasing needs for technically educated people. Reflecting this demand, the University of Vermont began to offer civil engineering courses in 1829 and Rensselaer Polytechnic Institute conferred its first degrees in science and engineering in 1835. These were the first breaks away from the traditional classical—or "liberal arts"—pattern of collegiate education. These also represented the first formalized expansion of the concept of engineering education outside the military field. This enlarged concept gradually has embraced the field then known as "mechanic arts."

With the passing of the Land-Grant Act in 1862 establishing the publicly financed colleges, and with the increased industrialization following the Civil War, there was a rapid growth in the number of agricultural colleges, state universities, and technical schools. The first Land-Grant Act of 1862 provided Federal funds for the endowment and maintenance of at least one college in each state where the objective should be ". . . to teach such branches of learning as are related to agriculture and the mechanic arts . . . in order to promote the liberal and practical education of the industrial classes in the several pursuits and professions of life." The second Land-Grant Act provided further for ". . . instruction of agriculture, the mechanic arts, the English language, and the various branches of mechanical, physical, natural, and economic science, with specific reference to their application to the industries of life, and to the facilities for such instruction."

Obviously, these two congressional acts intended that post-high school education at the collegiate level should be provided for persons seeking to prepare for careers in industrial and technical occupations. These acts and the collegiate system which grew out of them constituted a major and lasting influence toward a general recognition and acknowledgment of the importance and the academic respectability of technology as a vital element in higher education. Most of the presently recognized public engineering colleges in the United States have developed within this system, although no reference to "engineering" is to be found in the establishing acts. In addition to the public colleges, many private institutes and colleges were established through endowments from wealthy philanthropists during the last few decades of the nineteenth century and the earlier years of the twentieth. Most of these emphasized technical education. In addition, some of the church-supported liberal arts colleges introduced engineering programs.

Under the allurement of the subsequent mushroomlike growth of interest in collegiate engineering education, and because of the prestige and tangible results to be gained through the earning of a recognized baccalaureate degree, many of the early technical schools which served the equivalent functions of the present-day technical institutes during the early years of their development and growth later became four-year engineering colleges. Although some of the stronger technical institutes withstood this trend, the total number was substantially reduced. By 1922 there were only thirteen technical institutes. By 1928–1929, when the first national study[2] of technical institutes was made by Wickenden and Spahr, only thirty-one schools were offering curriculums then considered to be of technical institute character. These included both day and evening schools, eleven classified as public institutions and twenty as independent institutions. By 1954 Smith[3] found this number to have grown to sixty-nine. The present National Survey reveals that by 1957 the number had increased to 144. Of these 144 institutions, ninety-two are publicly tax-supported and fifty-two are private, either endowed or proprietary. Another group of forty-eight institutions indicated technical institute curriculums were offered, but their curriculum content revealed the courses were either vocational-technical or pre-engineering in nature. Of this gross total of 144 schools, 121 furnished data sufficiently complete to be useful for Survey purposes.

During the unsettled years of the 1920s and 1930s the concept of the junior college and community college slowly developed. Great impetus was given the movement by the unprecedented public support for junior colleges in California. The emphasis in higher education was on "liberal" study and "general" subject matter or on business programs, not on science, engineering, or technology. The junior college was nurtured under these conditions. Hence the major objective of most of these schools became the

[2] For a more complete history of the technical institute movement, see William E. Wickenden and Robert H. Spahr, *A Study of Technical Institutes*, Society for the Promotion of Engineering Education, Lancaster, Pa., 1931, and American Society for Engineering Education, University of Illinois, Urbana, Ill.

[3] Leo F. Smith and Laurence Lipsett, *The Technical Institute*, McGraw-Hill Book Company, Inc., New York, 1956.

provision of transfer courses to prepare their graduates for upper-class years at a university, principally in liberal arts or general studies.

By 1957–1958 the junior or community college in the United States was, with but minor exceptions, just at the threshold of a really significant participation in technical education. In potential, however, it cannot and should not be ignored, especially in the light of rapidly increasing national requirements for educational capacity. Basically, it is a multipurpose institution. In general, nationwide, it still is overwhelmingly concerned with general education objectives as represented by liberal arts and college-transfer programs. Too many of those schools currently showing interest in technical subject matter fail to distinguish between the content and philosophy required for an effective technical institute curriculum and the content and philosophy adequate for effective vocational-trade or "vocational-technical" curriculums and shop courses.

In substantial measure, this confusion is engendered by the proliferation of trade and industrial training in public schools and colleges through the use of Federal tax funds and through the movements by the state agencies which supervise the use of this money to promote the extension of this vocational training into the area of the engineering technician.

At the other extreme, many erroneously think that a pre-engineering program is the equivalent of a bona fide technical institute program. In any event, what the junior college in the United States can do, or should try to do, in the area of technological curriculums for engineering and other technicians depends entirely upon the circumstances, the leadership, and the philosophy controlling each individual institution. This is attested to by the fact that several splendid examples of well-designed and competently administered technical-institute-type programs were found among junior or community colleges, particularly in New York, California, and Texas.

In some of these instances, and particularly in New York, the entire program of a community college was found to be devoted to "applied science" as epitomized in the technical-institute-type curriculums, to the exclusion of a college-transfer program as such. In other instances, the technical-institute-type curriculums constituted only a part of the total program, but were handled both administratively and educationally with a clear understanding of the significant differences in scope and objective and with appropriate differences in nature and emphasis of curriculum content. Outstanding among this latter group is a city-operated community college in California which applied for and achieved Technical Institute Accreditation by the Engineers' Council for Professional Development for its entire group of curriculums in engineering technologies. This school is the first of the public junior colleges to seek and achieve this accreditation. Although several others could qualify, they continue to follow the established concept of the liberal-arts-dominated American junior college to look with disfavor upon any such professional recognition or accreditation. Continued adherence to such an idea imposes upon their technical graduates an increasingly handicapping stigma of substandard technological education. This is an unfortunate and unnecessary hurdle which the individual then has to overcome in seeking the employment for which he has studied.

The senior colleges and universities of the United States, with few exceptions, have occupied themselves with baccalaureate and advanced-degree programs to the exclusion of technological curriculums designed to develop qualified technicians in engineering and other subject fields. However, as of 1957–1958 the Survey found that an increasing number of colleges and universities are recognizing the significance and potential of this intermediate zone of higher education by current offerings of technical institute curriculums, or by current developments for early offering. Pioneers in this work include Purdue University, Pennsylvania State University, Oklahoma State University, University of Houston, University of Dayton, Georgia Institute of Technology, and North Carolina State College. Some of these technical institute programs are conducted in on-campus divisions; others have established separate campuses, largely because of fortuitous circumstances and available facilities. The Survey found both types of installation to be operating with equal effectiveness. In addition to these, a dozen or so other collegiate institutions were found to be offering curriculums or courses of a more or less similar general nature.

It is the non-tax-supported technical school which has provided leadership for intermediate technological education and given continuity to the "technical institute idea" of organized occupational curriculums since its early years of growth prior to the turn of the century. This is not surprising, for traditionally it has been the independent educational institution that has pioneered new concepts, new areas, and new methods of education. The independent institution occupies a position of special opportunity and responsibility because of its inherent tradition of relative freedom and flexibility in policy and procedure.

In any account of the development of technological education in the United States, it is necessary to acknowledge the fact that American industry as a whole has developed a tremendous internal training and educational program. These industrial programs range from trade apprenticeship training to the highest levels of collegiate graduate work. In subject matter, they range from manual-skill training to industrial management and from English and speech to nuclear theory. The universal objective is to develop available manpower to meet the needs of the individual enterprise. The National Survey of Technical Institute Education specifically refrained from any attempt to assay this huge phase of America's over-all pattern of education and training. This would be a task in itself. However, it must not be overlooked, especially when making international comparisons.

Historical background

Although the technical institute has grown out of the American culture and economy, the "idea" of the technical institute as it is known today was introduced into the United States educational pattern by Frederick Pratt in 1895. The idea was a direct adaptation from the well-established Technikum of Germany which had been personally visited and studied for just this purpose by Pratt and an assistant. The core of this idea was a curricular pattern built up of an integrated sequence of courses of mathematics, technological subject matter, and related shop and laboratory experimental work. The level and nature of the subject matter distinguished it from the vocational-trade[4]

---

[4] The vocational-trade area of educational effort as referenced in this report includes the trade and industrial programs as covered by Smith-Hughes Federal funds. The phrase "less than college grade" is commonly used in both state and Federal literature describing the programs eligible for these and related Federal tax funds. In con-

area of educational effort. The curricular continuity distinguished it from the lecture series and self-study pattern of the then popular "Mechanics Institute" or "Athenaeum" from which several of the prominent technical institutes have evolved. The basic two-year pattern, and the emphasis upon practical application of the emerging engineering sciences and of other sciences and technologies, distinguished it from the college and university pattern. The level of instruction and the entrance requirements distinguished it from the vocational high school, which then was beginning to emerge in United States secondary education.

For example, at Pratt Institute the first technical institute curriculums were designed for adults—mature and experienced industrial craftsmen of age thirty or so. Entrance requirements were such that even a high school graduate needed at least two years of industrial experience to qualify. This is of particular interest, because when Pratt Institute was first established in 1877, it was set up as a vocational high school and operated as such until 1892. In 1892, when New York City became interested in adding a vocational high school to its growing secondary system, the Pratt family turned over to the city its whole trade-technical-vocational program complete with faculty. This left the Pratt family with only their art school and "domestic science" school. These, however, served as the nucleus around which the work in engineering and scientific technologies, adapted from the German Technikum,

---

tradistinction, the technical institute curricular program as covered by this Survey is distinctly of "college grade" in level of entrance requirements and instruction, and it normally leads to the degree of Associate in Science, Associate in Applied Science, or Associate in Engineering.

was organized in the evolution and establishment of the "technical institute idea" of offering basically two-year applied-science curriculums as now known.

Factors affecting the growth of the technical institute

Since the beginning of World War II in 1939, rapid changes of technological, economic, and social significance have had a direct impact upon the interest in, and need for, technical institute education in the United States.

The principal influence is the tremendous magnitude and rapid rate of technological development in industry. This in turn reflects the expanding frontiers of new scientific knowledge and the growing necessity for more and more people to understand how to put it to work in everyday life. This rapid growth is most apparent in the electronic, aeronautical, mechanical, and chemical industries. As they now must function to continue in existence, these and related industries require a relatively large number of people having a considerable knowledge of the basic physical sciences and mathematics *plus* the ability and skill to apply this knowledge to industrial processes and related problems. The trend of this demand for technological personnel is reflected in the fact that within a relatively few years the requirement of United States industry for persons on its engineering staff has risen sharply from one for every 2000 employees to a 1957–1958 ratio of 1 to 50—and it is still growing. Much of the resulting demand for technological personnel is directly translatable into demand and opportunity for engineering technicians as defined in this report.

An intimately related factor is the shortage of competent technological manpower which grew to proportions dangerous to the national security during World War II and has continued since then. This has been variously expressed, but came widely to public attention in terms of a "shortage of scientists and engineers." However, as revealed by this Survey—and by task-force studies of the President's Committee on Scientists and Engineers—much of the actual shortage lay in the area of properly trained supporting personnel such as the engineering technician.

In addition to the high rate and great magnitude of technological developments and to the shortage of competent technological manpower, another factor directly affecting the growth and potential of the technical institute is the increasing stature and growing acceptance of the technical institute movement in higher education. This growth is illustrated by such items as:

1. The establishment in 1941 of the Technical Institute Division of the American Society for Engineering Education.

2. The accreditation of technical institute curriculums by the Engineers' Council for Professional Development. In 1944 ECPD accepted the responsibility for inspecting and evaluating technical institute programs, and it has functioned continuously since that time, paralleling its previously established activity for the evaluation and accreditation of engineering curriculums. As of 1958, a total of 116 technical institute curriculums were reported as accredited in 36 institutions in 17 states serving 53 different localities.

3. The growing practice among highly qualified schools of recognized standing of granting an associate degree for the completion of technical as well as general programs of two years' duration. In 1956 the American Society for Engineering Education endorsed the granting of the Associate in Engineering degree for the completion of accred-

ited two-year curriculums in engineering technologies; the Associate in Science degree and the Associate in Arts degree complete the presently recognized areas, paralleling the academic fields of the established four-year baccalaureate degrees.

4. Establishment in April, 1956, of the President's Committee on Scientists and Engineers, which included among its working groups one assigned specifically to study technical institute education.

5. Establishment in 1956–1957, by the State Highway Departments of California and Illinois, of classification "ladders" which give full recognition, status, and potential to the engineering technician in the engineering personnel organization.

6. Establishment in 1957 in the Province of Ontario, Canada, of a program which gives recognition and status to the engineering technician in coordination with the Association of Professional Engineers, the Provincial Government, and the industry of the province.

7. Establishment in 1957 of a Committee on Engineering Technicians and Technical Institute Education by the National Society of Professional Engineers.

8. The increasing public recognition and support for technical institute education, as illustrated by the founding of tax-supported technical institutes in Connecticut, Georgia, Indiana, Louisiana, New York, Michigan, Oklahoma, Oregon, North Carolina, and Pennsylvania.

9. The steady growth of a significant body of literature concerning technical institute education.[5]

[5] "Literature Significant to Education of the Technical Institute Type," comprehensive annotated bibliography, Technical Institute Division, American Society for Engineering Education, University of Illinois, Urbana, Ill., 1953.

10. Plans for the 1960 census to include much more information on technicians.

11. Recognition by the U.S. Civil Service Commission of technical institute graduation as part of requirements for many positions.

12. Preparation of Supplement to Dictionary of Occupational Titles by United States Employment Service, Department of Labor, covering several hundred technician jobs.

Socioeconomic influences have played their parts in the broadening trend in technical institute development. A factor strongly on the negative side has been the "sub" status to which both the engineering profession and engineering education have tended to relegate the technical institute idea. Fortunately this inherent opposition is softening in favor of a more realistic view, as indicated in the preceding paragraph. Influences on the positive side include:

1. Slowly growing public recognition of the fact that the achievement of rewarding competencies within the range of personal interests and aptitudes of the individual student is the true measure of the worth of an educational program, rather than some traditional number of years spent "in college" on traditional subject matter.

2. The significant economic fact that the employment market for competent engineering technician graduates of recognized two-year curriculums is good enough so that it may take the average engineering graduate from a traditional four-year curriculum fifteen years or more to catch up on the basis of accumulated net worth in dollars and cents including the higher cost of the education involved.[6]

[6] Some employers have adopted separate salary schedules for engineering technicians and engineers that have considerable overlap.

3. A trend toward earlier marriage and family responsibility, with consequent needs of young people for earlier development of remunerative employability in stimulating and satisfying areas of activity.

Trend

Until full and effective use is made of qualified and specifically educated technicians in the entire national complex of technological personnel, the "shortage" of engineers and scientists seems destined to continue or to get worse. For two compelling reasons the answer does not lie in the direction of expanding the universities and engineering colleges to produce an increasing proportion of graduate engineers and scientists:

1. Much of the work traditionally regarded as requiring a four-year engineering graduate is now being accomplished competently—in many instances better—by a qualified engineering technician;

2. National statistics clearly indicate that in spite of the publicized "exploding population," not enough persons are being born daily to go through the traditional educational cycle and provide the proportionate number of engineers and scientists which will be needed in everyday life on the basis of present traditional methods of education and utilization.

Regardless of such debates as may be heard involving the semantics or statistics of this situation, there is no dodging the fact that throughout the American industrial complex, severe shortages of adequate competencies in the right places have existed since 1945. These show no evidence of abating except where engineering technicians have been utilized. Such recent needs have been met mostly through emergency measures, which for everyone's advantage economically and sociologically should give way to an integrated plan of proper education and utilization of technological manpower.

The Survey finds that the technical institute idea in higher education has achieved in several significant areas of industrial and civil life a recognized standing in the general pattern of American education. Thus it gradually is being accorded status and recognition in keeping with the significance of its demonstrated potential as an avenue through which a greater proportion of young men and women may, according to their individual interests and aptitudes, learn productive and rewarding occupations and thus be better citizens.

CHAPTER 2

Philosophy and Objective
of the Technical Institute

THE BASIC OBJECTIVE of the technical institute idea in higher education is the development of qualified engineering technicians proficient in a selected field of technology. Thus the technical institute curricular program leads to a specific objective just as any collegiate program does. In general, the technical institute program is designed to accomplish its objective within two academic years. Some programs are longer, some have been shorter.[1] For completing this program, the technical institute student usually is awarded the associate degree.

By way of emphasis, a contrast should be noted. The technical institute program is not intended as a feeder channel to the university. The program is not comparable to the first two years of a four-year engineering program —it is much more than that in some important respects

[1] Since October, 1958, the Engineers' Council for Professional Development has considered for accreditation only those technical institute curriculums that extend over two academic years or the equivalent, but is continuing to accredit programs of up to three academic years in length.

and somewhat less in others; its direction and emphasis are significantly different. In the sometimes confusing parlance of educators, the technical institute program therefore is commonly referred to as a "terminal" program. This causes many qualified people to shy away from it, mistakenly. The technical institute program is no more terminal than any other collegiate degree program. It is terminal only in that it is not specifically designed to meet the limiting requirements characteristic of most college and university catalogues for transfer credits or to prepare an individual for graduate studies. The bona fide technical institute program is designed instead to give the student a high degree of proficiency in his chosen field of technology, solidly supported by a sound working knowledge of the mathematics, English, basic science, and technological principles involved in that field.

At the same time, however, it should be recorded that as time goes on, an increasing number of senior colleges and universities are giving advanced standing to technical institute graduates in a variety of four-year programs. In many instances, on a selective basis, two full years of credit are being given toward baccalaureate degrees, especially in the areas of communications curriculums, industrial education, and other nonengineering areas. As far as this practice concerns the basic objective of the technical institute, it is considered to be a byproduct which properly takes care of the exceptional student or the special circumstance.

The philosophy of the technical institute idea is that for every young person who has the capacity, incentive, and resources to pursue formal technological education to a bachelor's or more advanced degree, there are many who have the right capacity, interest, and aptitude to develop productive and rewarding careers in the expanding realm

of applied science and the technologies which neither require nor justify four or more years of collegiate study. It
is the function and the challenging opportunity of the
technical institute idea in higher education to serve these
people through properly designed curriculums in appropriately specialized fields of subject matter.

Definitions

For the purposes of the National Survey of Technical Institute Education, the following two definitions were developed. They became widely distributed during the course
of the Survey in 1956–1958 and have been adopted in
whole or in substance by an increasing number of educational, industrial, and professional agencies.

The engineering technician

In general, the engineering technician is a person whose
chief interests and activities lie in the direction of the testing and development, the application, and the operation
of engineering and scientific equipment and processes.
Classified on the basis of educational certification, the engineering technician would be a graduate of a technical institute type of curriculum as accredited by the Engineers'
Council for Professional Development, or recognized equivalent. Classified occupationally, the engineering technician
performs semiprofessional functions of an engineering or
scientific nature, largely upon his own initiative and under
only general supervision of a professional engineer or scientist; he assists the engineer or scientist and supplements
his work.

Typical among the wide array of semiprofessional functions performed by engineering and scientific technicians

are: drafting, design, and development of products and of engineering plant; installing and operating equipment; estimating costs; selling; and advising customers on the use of engineering or scientific equipment.

In many instances, the technician may serve as a liaison between the engineer or scientist, on the one hand, and the skilled craftsman or layman on the other hand. In carrying out these various activities, he may have group leadership responsibilities. Therefore, the technician must be able to communicate mathematically, scientifically, and linguistically.

Technical institute education

The term refers to the intermediate strata of technical curriculums which are from one[1] to three years' duration (full time) beyond the high school level. Curriculums are technological in nature, and they differ in both content and purpose from those of the vocational school on the one hand, and from those of the engineering college on the other hand.

Such curriculums emphasize the understanding and practical application of basic principles of mathematics and science rather than the acquisition of proficiency in manual skills. High school graduation is required for admission, and mathematics through algebra and geometry is prerequisite.

The programs of instruction are similar in nature to professional engineering curriculums but briefer and more completely technical in content. The major purpose is to prepare individuals for various technical positions or specialized areas of activity encompassed within the broad field of engineering enterprise.

Relationships in educational spectrum

In considering the proper place of the technical institute program in the national educational and professional spectrum, attention must be focused upon the fact that it is the engineering field which has exploded. As the results of scientific research complicate the tasks to be performed by the engineer (whether he be in development, production, or construction) and carry the field of the engineer farther and farther away from the realms of application and operation in which modern engineering started, two facts stand out with increasing clarity.

The first fact is that some adequate and integrated provision must be made to continue to supply the technically competent manpower required for this engineering application and operation, and required also to augment and to supplement the professional engineer and the scientist in research, design, development, and supervision. This manpower is a part of the over-all engineering manpower spectrum. In general effect, it is taking the place of "the engineer" as we have known him, as "the engineer" of today and of tomorrow increasingly takes his new place and becomes more and more devoted to the scientific problems and opportunities of the expanding technological universe. This manpower area is the professional area of the "engineering technician."

The second fact is that, for his optimum development, the engineering technician is best served by an educational program which is intimately related to, but which differs significantly from, the program most effective for the engineer, and which likewise differs significantly from the educational program most effective in developing or enhancing the skills and the "know-how" of the craftsman. The engineering technician does *not* need either the depth or the extent of mathematical or scientific understanding required by the engineer. However, the engineering technician *does* need to have a practical working understanding of essentially the same subject matter, together with appropriate communication skills and mathematical competence. To achieve the necessary results, an educational approach is required that is comparable in quality and general level to the university-collegiate engineering program, but that differs significantly in emphasis, which is that of practical application of established scientific principles rather than the development of new design concepts or the extension of existing knowledge.

Further, in contrast to the craftsman and his appropriate educational program of vocational-trade skills and related subject matter, the engineering technician does *not* benefit significantly from the development of proficiency in manual or manipulative skills nor from technological subject matter taught from that angle. However, the engineering technician *does* need to have a general working knowledge and appreciation of the manufacturing or operational skills related to his area of occupational and subject-matter interest. For uncompromised results, this requires an educational approach distinctly different from and much more academically rigorous and technical than the skill-proficiency program effective for the training of the craftsman and commonly represented in the vocational-trade or vocational-technical programs which have evolved in tax-supported secondary schools and colleges under the Smith-Hughes Vocational Education Act.

The country-wide consensus among the Regional Committees of the National Survey is overwhelmingly to the effect that the technical institute educational program, as defined and as currently needed, lies much closer to the professional levels of engineering than to the trade-skill and craft level of the vocational program. Here, it should be clearly understood that this is in no way a criticism of vocational education or the currently upgraded trade-training programs, nor a reflection upon them, but merely a statement of proper relationship. There is strong evidence that these critical distinctions too often are confused.

A further comment is in order concerning the relationship existing between acceptable technical institute curriculums and the typical basic preprofessional curriculums of the junior college or lower-division collegiate curriculums leading to the engineering degree. At the risk of oversimplification, it may be said emphatically that the person who finishes the first two years of an engineering curriculum as presently catalogued by most of the ECPD-accredited engineering colleges and universities is *not* adequately prepared for productive employment as an engineering technician or an engineer. Survey consensus is that such a person has too much of too little to qualify as an engineering technician on the one hand, while, on the other hand, he is only at the threshold of his professional engineering education.

Another point of major importance causes considerable confusion. This is the misguided idea that the zone of the engineering technician is the natural "dumping ground" for those who "can't make the grade" in engineering. This misunderstanding is unfortunately common among the counselors of students at both secondary and collegiate level. Survey consensus is that most of those unfortunate misfits who cannot make the grade in engineering would be just as miserable misfits in the field of the engineering technician. Consequently, the field of the engineering technician is no more logically to be considered the "dumping ground" for misfit engineers than is the field of engineering logically to be considered as the "dumping ground" for misfit Ph.D.s or physical scientists. These interrelated fields of human endeavor are coequal in their importance to the whole social and economic—and professional—structure. They and the people in them—and the people who should be in them to provide the effective and satisfying balance of manpower distribution needed for our way of life—deserve to be accorded interrelated status and recognition.

Better manpower balance

Just as a large and growing segment of the engineering science of yesterday has become today's technology and as such is competently handled by qualified engineering technicians, so will much of today's expanding science become tomorrow's technology. As the frontiers of engineering science move on, there must be an ever-growing supply of competent manpower to keep the over-all engineering enterprise operating and growing. Recognition of the technical institute idea in higher education provides a logical channel for the expansion of total technological manpower without any "watering-down" or down-grading.

The quantitative aspects of this situation may be indicated by the fact that in the present national economy there is a confirmed need for qualified and properly prepared technicians in engineering and related technologies which numerically exceeds the much-talked-about need for scientists and engineers. From this fact it follows that one of the productive ways to increase the effective total supply of engineering-scientific manpower is to coordinate the development and utilization of the engineering technician with the development and utilization of the engineer. This presumes the courage to turn over to the engineering technician those segments of yesterday's engineering and science which have become today's technologies. And it must be recognized that these are very large segments.

Turning over technology to technicians methodically and determinedly would multiply correspondingly the time and energies of qualified engineering-scientific manpower. This manpower, then, could extend and expand its competence and creative abilities into the frontier problems of today's science and tomorrow's engineering. This transfer of duties would conserve manpower, since, for example, only two years of curricular work are required to develop an engineering technician in contrast with the requirements of four or more years to develop the engineer or scientist. Further, by such a program to develop persons qualified to be engineering technicians, account is taken of that somewhat intangible but very important factor of the personal and community value of having such persons in jobs in keeping with their interests and aptitudes.

Changing times require changing concepts

Conditions have changed drastically in the relatively short history of engineering enterprise and still are changing. Frontiers have moved and still are moving. Manpower concepts, both social and professional, must keep pace. Both the concepts and the procedures relative to engineering science and related technologies, as they affect the entire spectrum of technological manpower both educationally and professionally, obviously must change accordingly. In fact, continuous planning and progressive action on a coordinated basis should anticipate rather than follow such established needs for manpower in our society. This is a challenge alike to engineering education and to the engineering profession.

History reminds us that the earliest area of organized and coordinated human endeavor which can be called "engineering" was, as might be expected, military. Mechanical ingenuity, meager technical knowledge, and manual skills were coordinated with brain power to devise "engines" and facilities for military purposes—the Trojan horse, for example. Later, human ingenuity and growing knowledge were used to design and construct roads, bridges, aqueducts, and other facilities for the civilian population. This development was called "civil" engineering to distinguish it from the military. Then came mechanical and electrical engineering and the broadening range of applied arts and sciences as the store of technical knowledge grew. All this is known—as history—but how often is it considered thoughtfully in the light of its ever-evolving sociological and educational impact?

In early days men engaged in engineering did not object to being called "electricians" or "mechanics." Even Charles P. Steinmetz, the "wizard" of early electrical science and education, was mentioned in the literature of his day as an "electrician." In fact, what about the engineering colleges? The land-grant college system, which today includes many renowned engineering schools, was established to create colleges of "agriculture and *mechanic arts*"—no mention of "engineering." However, as the fields expanded, there came a change. Professional consciousness took form, and professional-technical societies were founded —partly for self-education and partly for mutual prestige and promotion. Even in engineering education it may be recalled that before the turn of the century the Society for the Promotion of Engineering Education was formed. Note the word "promotion." Even less than seventy years ago, engineering education itself was fighting for a niche of recognition and acknowledgment of respectability in the cloistered halls of traditional higher education. Today, technical institute education is in a similar situation with respect to public and professional understanding and acceptance.

And that raises another question which is not too well settled: Just what is an "engineer"? Fifty years ago the scope of available technological and scientific information was of such proportions that the traditional four-year engineering curriculums had a fair chance to cover the ground reasonably well. With continuing expansion of technical knowledge and growing realization of the new knowledge still to be learned or digested for later application, the engineering spectrum, educationally as well as professionally, must be reevaluated and redivided—for example, as implied in the recent ASEE "Grinter Report." [2]

Manpower relationships—the engineering team

As previously mentioned, the famous Charles P. Steinmetz was referred to in contemporary literature as an "electrician" although he was an outstanding mathematician and authority on electrical and related science. In a way he represented the old "seat-of-the-pants" school—like Kettering, Edison, Ford, the Wright brothers, and many others —learning things by doing them and then similarly teaching others. In those days such people were, initially at least, "one-man teams" in so far as engineering explorations were concerned. Even as they developed beyond the initial

[2] *Report on Evaluation of Engineering Education,* American Society for Engineering Education, University of Illinois, Urbana, Ill., 1955.

stages, the individual could do the handwork as well as the brain work required, with the aid of supporting craftsmen; Mr. Bell and Mr. Watson of telephone fame, for example. Thus, with minor oversimplification, we can say evolved the "two-man team" of engineer plus craftsman to accomplish an engineering project.

Times change, however, and a realization is beginning to develop that the national habit of unplanned growth has led to a persistence of effort to utilize a two-part team (the engineer plus the craftsman) beyond the ability of such a team to cope with the currently expanded—and ever-expanding—technology of our daily life.

In the two-man team pattern, the engineer or scientist must take time to do for himself many tasks associated with his work which do not require or justify his time or talents. Moreover, in many instances today such work would be done even better by a competent aide such as is envisioned in the engineering technician. The time and effort of the engineer or scientist thus saved would directly enhance his productive capacity and hence his earning power and personal satisfaction. This, too, would contribute substantially to a correction of the "shortage" of scientific-engineering manpower.

So, at long last, we are beginning to give serious national recognition to the need for a three-man team (the engineer, *plus* the technician, *plus* the craftsman) in the effective execution of an engineering project. This could be a major and lasting answer to our national problem of adequate technical and scientific manpower.

Recognition of the need for the three-part engineering team in industry has, of course, influenced the philosophy and objectives of technical education in the United States and Canada. For it is now clear that to produce efficiently an adequate supply of qualified manpower for the three-part engineering-scientific team, we shall require a three-part educational program:

1. The university-collegiate program for engineers and scientists
2. The technical institute program for engineering and scientific technicians
3. The vocational-trade programs for craftsmen and apprenticeship

Evolution of philosophy and objectives of technical institute education

The philosophy and objective of technical institute education have experienced a somewhat erratic and uneven development in the United States and Canada, related, of course, to the historical events traced briefly in Chapter 1. Technical institute education as a distinct form of education came onto the scene early, antedating engineering education as such. But the rapid growth induced by the twin forces of industrialization and westward movement of frontiers may be regarded as having sidetracked a correspondingly rapid development of technical institute education. Perhaps someday an historical and sociological analysis of technology will reveal what happened to the philosophy of technical institute education during the period of its apparent eclipse when the introduction and rapid acceleration of engineering education dominated in the latter half of the nineteenth and early part of the twentieth century. Perhaps as a nation we leapfrogged this area of education while trying to make greater advances in the professional engineering field. Now, there is a compelling need to fill the gap.

Exactly when and how some public attention again

began to focus on technical institute education is not presently clear. The important consideration, however, is that the need for the engineering and scientific technician has become clear. The dramatic events of World War II only accentuated an inevitable development that was implicit, albeit somewhat obscured from general view, in the acceleration of technological change and rapid closure of the time lag between scientific discovery and engineering application. In many respects, the philosophy and practice of technical institute education were ready and waiting for recognition of the need for a more general acceptance and conscious utilization of the engineering and scientific technician. Certainly this is clear from the findings of Wickenden and Spahr thirty years ago. It is also evident from findings of this Survey, as later chapters will reveal, that one of the biggest inhibitors of more effective utilization of manpower is not lack of an appropriate kind of educational program, but lack of recognition among employers and the public of the practical rewards and social benefits that stem from use of the three-part engineering-scientific team. The philosophy of technical institute education stands already formulated, its objective patterned and developed through practice, its effective application dependent upon a better understanding.

As a final word, it should be remembered that the basic concept of the three-part team is by no means new or indigenous to the United States and Canada. Spahr and Wickenden called it to public attention in the United States about thirty years ago through their study and report. But they did not discover it, though in one sense they may be said to have rediscovered it. Both the concept and general pattern had long before become established in the technically proficient nations of Europe. Europe was the seed bed from which the concept was brought to the United States before the turn of the century. The idea did "take" and a native philosophy began to evolve, but in a scattered and desultory manner. Perhaps this slow evolution was due, in part at least, to the fact that the engineering profession itself was then preoccupied with its own struggle for recognition in the same general technological area, sometimes called "applied science." If circumstances had been such as to foster acceptance and development of the technical institute idea and its coordination in the American pattern of higher education and professional concept, perhaps the present "shortage" of technological manpower would not be as severe—or would not have occurred.

CHAPTER 3

The Technical Institute Curriculum

ONE WAY TO IDENTIFY the principles upon which technical institute curriculums should be based is to restate the basic objective of the technical institute idea in higher education. That is: to give to a qualified student a practical working knowledge of fundamental principles in a selected technical field. The scope of the curriculum must be sufficient to enable him to apply his talents effectively and satisfyingly and to coordinate his work with others within that field. The direct objective is the development of competence for gainful employment. "Gainful" here means not only monetary remuneration, but also the satisfaction and inspiration which can be earned by an individual only through productive performance in a challenging occupation within the range of his interests and aptitudes.

Another way to identify the principles upon which technical institute curriculums should be based is to describe the results sought through technical institute education. Technical institute curriculums should:

1. Be directed toward a specific occupational area which is sufficiently attractive to draw qualified students. Such an

area normally will embrace a cluster, or group, of occupations related to the same basic industry or technology. Occupational competence is an essential objective of each curriculum (see Appendix 2).

2. Place emphasis upon a sound understanding and appreciation of the basic principles and established scientific facts specifically related to the selected subject field.

3. Place emphasis upon practical application of established mathematical, scientific, and technological principles rather than upon their derivation or theoretical development.

4. Contain appropriate courses in communications and other general subject matter carefully selected to suit the objectives of the specific curriculum. The engineering and scientific technician must be able to communicate scientifically and mathematically and, to do this effectively, he must be able to express himself linguistically and graphically.

5. Be developed or offered only in accordance with established needs. Curriculums should be offered only in specific occupational fields where demand, either present or potential, for graduates has definitely been established and identified (see Appendix 5).

6. Be developed in scope of content and in level of technical rigor to suit the capacity of the type of students whose enrollment is sought.

7. Be organized and presented in such a manner as to give the student a clear realization of the fact that although he is receiving a sound preparaton in the essentials of his selected technology, his personal growth and advancement after graduation will depend upon his continuing effort to broaden his field of knowledge and understanding.

The technical institute curriculum is aimed principally

at the development of intellectual capacity, supplemented by development of directly related manual skills. This is in contrast with the craft or vocational-trade curriculum which is aimed at the development of a high degree of proficiency in manual skill, supplemented by a general understanding of the fundamentals of related subject matter. This is also in contrast with the present trend in engineering and science curriculums, which aims at the development of an extended intellectual capacity rather than manual skills. In the technical institute curriculum, such shop work as may be included is primarily for demonstration purposes. A full range of appropriate laboratory experience constitutes an important part of the technical institute curriculum, closely integrated with classroom instruction for the development and solution of practical problems.

Industrial correlation

To fulfill its obligation, the technical institute curriculum must mold and develop the attitudes and aptitudes of the student toward optimum proficiency and productive capacity for immediate employment. By its very nature, the technical institute curriculum is a meeting ground where the mutual interests of the employer, the student, and the educational institution may be brought together. Thus, the participation of industry[1] is vitally important in designing a technical institute curriculum.

The common objective of all technical institutes is to prepare students for competence in a cluster of related technical occupations. This imposes an obligation upon the technical institute educator to *know* what specific knowledge and skills are required for competence in the

[1] In this report the word "industry" is used as a generic term covering all areas of technological employment.

occupational areas selected for curricular development. Such information can be obtained only by knowledge of what industry requires and what the actual demand is for graduates from any particular curriculum. The vital need for the technical institute, therefore, is to establish and maintain close liaison through advisory committees or staff contacts with the industry it presumes to serve. Only through meeting its share of the technological manpower needs can the technical institute fulfill its obligation to its students and the community. By virtue of the objectives of the technical institute, its curriculums are more closely related to the needs of industry than are engineering curriculums on the one hand, which prepare for a broader professional approach, or the vocational-trade school curriculums on the other hand, which prepare for a specific type of job.

The really significant aspect of the technical institute idea is in its relatively localized application. Hence, the selection of curriculums should be directly geared to the needs and opportunities of the service area for which the school assumes—or aspires to assume—responsibility. These needs can be ascertained in any of several ways. The most obvious method occurs when an interested group of industries studies its own needs for technically trained personnel and brings specific proposals to the attention of school authorities. Frequently the needs are less obvious, especially in areas where industry is diversified or made up of relatively small units of varying natures and needs. In such instances the necessity for a thorough survey is indicated, to reveal qualitatively as well as quantitatively just what is required. But, whatever the local situation may be, the establishment and maintenance of direct liaison and close mutual understanding between school and industry is essential.

Technique of curriculum construction

In the growing literature pertaining to the technical institute one fact is clear: there is no one method of curriculum construction which is best for every situation. In practice, technical institutes commonly have made effective use of a combination of methods. The several methods may be outlined as follows:[2]

Scissors and paste-pot

In education, as in other pursuits, there are more followers than pioneers. An unfortunately common approach to curriculum construction is this method in which existing curriculums in the same field are examined and adopted, in whole or in part.

Opinion analysis

A slightly more penetrating approach is to obtain the opinion of experts about curriculum content. Technical institutes using this method commonly draw upon both educators and industrial experts for ideas and contributory experiences.

Deductive method

This method involves starting with the institute's objectives and from them determining the change in students' knowledge, skills, and attitudes which the curricu-

[2] Leo F. Smith and Laurence Lipsett, *The Technical Institute*, McGraw-Hill Book Company, Inc., New York, 1956, p. 130.

lum will attempt to bring about. The course content then is deduced by a logical reasoning process.

Inductive method

This method emphasizes activity analysis. The several occupational and nonoccupational activities for which students are to be prepared are identified. Then these activities are studied by firsthand observation, by examining job descriptions and other such information, and by obtaining information and experience reports from experts concerning the scope and depth of activities involved. On the basis of the activities thus analyzed (Appendix 5), an inductive reasoning process is used to determine the knowledge, skills, and other factors which should be included in the curriculum to achieve its objective.

Perhaps because of their common occupational focus, technical institutes traditionally have pioneered in the inductive method, particularly in the matter of techniques of job analysis. By consensus this is regarded as being the most effective approach. It is the one used most commonly among established technical institutes, sometimes with appropriate admixtures from the others.

Where a curriculum is designed inductively from activity analysis, the basic step is to ascertain both the requirements for initial employment and the requirements for advancement. These requirements can be ascertained most readily through the preparation of a "target group" of job titles or descriptions to be found in the technological area under consideration. These should be procured from industry within the service area of the school by direct contact and discussion so that proper evaluation and interpretation may be made and a mutual understanding established. This process will indicate supplementary or divergent occupations as well as the basic occupations requiring knowledge and proficiency in the particular technology under consideration. Examples of typical job titles as related to the several technological areas are presented in Appendix 2. Familiarity with this general pattern should be of direct help to school people in identifying what they should look for in their contacts with industry. Even in the best circumstances, unfortunately, great variations in terminology and definition are to be found. But these need not be seriously confusing if jobs are described operationally.

Curriculum content

In evaluating the content of any particular curriculum, the subject matter listing is but one of the four factors which must be considered in any qualitative decision. The other three factors are (1) the adequacy of the faculty, quantitatively, qualitatively, and in the soundness of their understanding of the technical institute objective; (2) adequacy and appropriateness of instructional material and equipment; (3) evaluation of the performance of graduates. The purpose of this section, however, is to discuss only curriculum content.

A major strong point in the philosophy of the technical institute lies in its idea of controlled flexibility which enables each curriculum to be developed and evolved according to changing needs. The resulting diversity among institutes makes the presentation here of any "average" curriculum misleading. However, the representative samples given in Appendix 3 indicate the general scope and nature of currently effective curriculums. Comparative data pertaining to the relative emphasis given to the several major classifications of subject matter are given in Appendix 4.

Another approach to the analysis of content of currently active technical institute curriculums is given in Table 3-1. These data were compiled by the Committee on Curriculum Development of the Technical Institute Division of the American Society for Engineering Education. The source of these data was a questionnaire study covering curriculums accredited by the Engineers' Council for Professional Development. These tabulations reveal the average percentage of time devoted to the different component groups of subject matter.

The place of mathematics

Mathematics plays a major role in the technical institute curriculum. It is the language of engineering-scientific technology. It is one of the four methods of communication in which the engineering or scientific technician must be appropriately proficient; the others are scientific, linguistic, and graphical. The nature and level of the mathematical content is a major line of demarcation between the vocational-trade, or vocational-technical, program and the technical institute curriculum. The prevailing general practice is to require proficiency in high school algebra and geometry and sometimes trigonometry as an entrance requirement. The scope of mathematics in the technical institute curriculum varies according to the objectives of the specific curriculum. The range is from a minimum of elementary college algebra and plane trigonometry for a curriculum such as construction technology to analytic geometry and elementary calculus for curriculums in mechanical design or electronics.

TABLE 3-1

Analysis of ECPD-accredited Curriculums for the Year 1957

(Questionnaire by Curriculum Development Committee, Technical Institute Division, ASEE)

Curriculum technology groups	Average percentage of total hours for 1957									
	Basic sciences (includes math)		Major technical specialty		Allied technical specialties		Administrative and managerial subjects		General subjects	
	Contact	Credit	Contact	Credit	Contact	Credit	Contact	Credit	Contact	Credit
Aeronautics design—maintenance and production	10.6	15.8	67.1	62.8	13.3	16.3	6.5	1.1	2.4	4.0
Air conditioning, heating, and refrigeration	14.3	20.6	45.6	43.0	27.7	20.3	2.3	3.2	10.1	12.9
Architecture, building construction	16.8	23.8	38.0	37.1	34.7	23.6	3.0	4.2	7.5	11.3
Civil	16.6	21.7	63.9	54.8	12.4	12.1	0.4	1.5	6.7	9.9
Electronics, radio, and television	15.2	18.5	70.3	65.5	7.9	6.0	1.8	3.0	4.8	7.0
Industrial electricity	20.2	24.4	47.1	44.4	18.4	12.4	2.9	4.0	11.3	14.8
Mechanical technologies	27.5	31.4	31.0	26.4	23.9	19.4	6.1	7.4	11.5	15.4
Steam, diesel, and automotive	20.7	27.4	36.8	33.5	33.2	26.6	3.5	5.0	5.8	7.5
Other	18.2	25.8	36.4	40.0	34.5	18.4	4.8	6.6	6.1	9.2
Average percentage	17.8	23.2	48.5	45.4	22.9	17.2	3.5	4.0	7.3	10.2

Technical institute mathematics is characteristically taught as a separate course, independent of other technical subject matter. However, it is not taught in the abstract, as mathematics for mathematics' sake. Established principles and procedures are emphasized rather than theoretical derivations and proofs. Independence from other technical subject matter is tempered by appropriate coordination so that the student develops an appreciation of mathematics as a necessary and useful tool in the technology of his choice.

Survey data show that the emphasis currently being given to mathematics ranges from 4 to 19 (median 12.5) per cent of the total semester credit hours for ECPD-accredited curriculums, depending upon the objective of the specific curriculum and the philosophy of the individual school (Appendix 3).

Survey visitations with industries and technical institutes revealed a current trend toward a higher percentage of time for, and a more rigorous presentation in, mathematics in the technical institute curriculum, as the technician becomes more deeply involved in working with engineers and scientists. This trend apparently results from specific demands from industry and from progress reports from graduates.

The place of the physical sciences

In response to a growing demand for a somewhat broader base of understanding in the various technologies, there is some current trend toward increased emphasis on physics in technical institute curriculums. One educator puts it this way:

Instruction in physics is the cornerstone of all our technical institute curriculums. All technical majors take a full year of physics as freshmen. This course, which we call "technical physics," carries four units of credit each semester for three demonstration lectures and three hours of laboratory work a week . . . the course emphasizes mechanics, heat, and electricity, but includes an elementary treatment of sound, light, and atomic physics . . . special emphasis is placed on industrial measurement, heat engines, and electricity including elementary electronics. . . . Every opportunity is taken to make physics meaningful by a judicious selection of problems from industry. . . . The necessity for a strong program in physics at the pre-engineering level has long been recognized. Technician education demands an equally strong physics program, but it must be especially adapted to the needs of the technical institute student. . . .[3]

Survey data show that the emphasis currently being given to basic science ranges from 3 to 15 (median 9) per cent of total semester credit hours for ECPD-accredited curriculums, depending upon the objective of the specific curriculum and the philosophy of the individual school. The amount and nature of basic science included may affect the proportion of time required for both the major and allied technical specialties.

A tendency in some schools, notably junior colleges, to offer a large proportion of physics or other basic science in lieu of appropriate specialized technical subject matter should be guarded against. Another tendency in some schools—to consolidate the student body into fewer and larger units to be served by common courses in "general science" or "general technology"—is understandable from

[3] N. C. Harris, "The Role of Physics in Technical Education," *Technical Education News*, April, 1955.

an economic and administrative viewpoint, but it is not to be recommended educationally. Inherently the engineering technician is a specialist, highly developed in a technological area of relatively limited extent. The Survey found little, if any, evidence from industry which indicated a need for a "general" engineering technician, which is the resultant product of such consolidation.

The place of shop and laboratory

In a technical institute curriculum the shop serves as a laboratory supplementing classroom instruction. Its purpose is to provide introduction to related techniques and practical manufacturing or construction problems, and general understanding of them, rather than to develop proficiency in manual skills as would be the case in the vocational-trade curriculum. On this basis, appropriate shop work and related instructional equipment would seem to have an established and continuing place in the well-balanced technical institute curriculum. The present trend in the development of college curriculums leading to the baccalaureate degree in engineering is toward the complete elimination of all shops. This ranges all the way from foundries and machine shops, which once were the proud mark of the college mechanical engineering department, to the field surveying of the civil engineering department. This trend in engineering education toward a more scientific level of curriculum content poses a need and opportunity for the technical institute curriculum to fill the gap. Generally speaking, the appropriately equipped laboratory is an inseparable part of the technical institute curriculum.

The place of general education and communications courses

In the earlier years of this century, technical institutes as a group devoted meager time and attention to courses in the social sciences, humanities, English, or communications. Paralleling the growth of interest on the part of engineering educators in the social-humanistic stem of the curriculum, technical institute educators also have been giving increased attention to this area.

There appears to be general agreement that work with the English language as an instrument of communication is especially necessary. Currently, English or communications courses account for a range of from 1 to 12 per cent (median 5 per cent) of the total semester credit hours in ECPD-accredited curriculums. This attention to language skills stems from the fact that the engineering technician often serves as a liaison between the engineer or scientist on the one hand, and the skilled craftsman or customer on the other. Also he is finding an ever-widening place in line or group supervision. Typically, a prime part of an engineering technician's work will involve the collection and correlation of data and the preparation of reports, specifications, and other communications which for effectiveness must be both accurate and lucid. Also he will have to receive such data and information and be able to translate them into operations understandable to others. Thus it becomes clear that as a part of his technical education the engineering technician must learn to use the language accurately and effectively.

There is less general agreement about the place of broader general education courses in technical institute curriculums. Consensus among experienced technical institute educators is that the scientific and technical demands are so great in a two-year program that there is not time to provide the proportion of general education which a four-year program may provide. It is felt that the prime requirement and obligation of a two-year technical curriculum is to assure to the student a thorough understanding of the scientific and technical fundamentals most significantly related to his selected field of technology.

Others among liberal arts educators, and particularly the specialists in social-humanistic studies, argue that one of the reasons the public has been so slow to accord the technical institute its proper place in the spectrum of higher education has been the reluctance of the institutes to undertake to provide more than technical education in their limited two-year span. This group holds that all segments of American education share an obligation to prepare young men and women for participation in our democratic society, that the higher the education, the greater the obligation, and that only general subject matter can accomplish this result.

Whatever the outcome of this debate may be, the present study shows that courses which may be classified as general education, including courses in communications, occupy a range of 0 to 12 per cent (median 3 per cent) of the total semester credit hours in curriculums currently accredited by ECPD. Additional evidence of the interest of technical institute educators in this problem is the fact that in 1953 the Technical Institute Division of the ASEE set up a Committee on General Education in the Technical Institute Curriculum.

At the 1954 annual meeting of this division of the ASEE,

Booher[4] reported on a survey of general education in technical institutes. He studied the catalogues of forty-eight institutes and surveyed 249 curricula. He found "the average time devoted to general education in all 249 curricula was 9.6 per cent of the total time (contact-hours) required to complete the courses, with the range extending from 0 to 35 per cent." Booher also found that in the ECPD-accredited curriculums the average time (contact-hours) allotted was 9.36 per cent, with a range from 0 to 23 per cent. In the non-ECPD-accredited curriculums, an average of 5.51 per cent of the time (contact hours) was devoted to general education, with a range from 0 to 35 per cent. The high percentages apply to New York State institutions. The eleven New York State institutes were studied separately because they all grant the Associate in Applied Science degree, for which the State Education Department has established certain requirements in general education. In these eleven institutes, Booher found that the average percentage of total curriculum contact hours devoted to general education was 20.3 with a range from 15.5 to 32.

In New York, in order to obtain the Associate in Applied Science degree, 20 semester credit hours in "General Education" subjects are required. Six of these are specified to be in English communication, six in the social sciences, six in mathematics or basic science, and two may be elected. The state is rigorous in its interpretation and, if

[4] Edward E. Booher, "Survey of General Education in Technical Institutes," *Technical Education News*, vol. XIV, special issue 1954, p. 6. Readers interested in the problem of general education in technical institutes are referred to the articles by Karl O. Werwath, C. L. Foster, Philip C. Martin, and Francis E. Almstead in the same issue.

an institution insists upon giving "Applied Mathematics" or "Related Chemistry," etc., the state may allow only half credit toward meeting the general education requirement.

On the basis of the subjects classified by New York State as "general education," most technical institute curriculums already have a higher percentage of such subject matter than at first meets the eye—for that matter, more than shows up in Tables 3-1 and 3-2 and in other exhibits including curriculum breakdowns given in Appendix 4.

Curriculum length

The matter of time requirement is an important question in the design of a technical institute curriculum. Obviously, it directly affects the amount and quality of instruction. Hence, it is pertinent to recognize that the prime objective of the technical institute curriculum is to develop in the student a high level of occupational proficiency within a restricted area of subject matter and to do this in the minimum time that will produce an effective result. Naturally, all these criteria are flexible and subject to opinion and circumstances.

The accreditation program by the Engineers' Council for Professional Development established in 1944 accepted one academic year as the minimum time required for a technical institute curriculum. This is based upon full-time work, or an equivalent total of part-time work—usually the equivalent of 32 semester credit hours. Since 1944, however, there has been a pronounced trend toward the establishment of two-year curriculums, this undoubtedly influenced by the growing general recognition of two-year curriculums in junior colleges and through the award of Associate degrees as approved in 1956 by the American Society for Engineering Education.

Since October, 1958, ECPD has accepted for technical institute accreditation nothing shorter than two-year curriculums.

The Survey study of some thirty-three ECPD-accredited curriculums and some seventy-three nonaccredited curriculums reflecting reasonable similarity of quality and purpose shows that:

1. The median for accredited curriculums is 76 semester credit hours (1944 contact hours) with 68.5 per cent of the total number of such curriculums clustered within 20 per cent above or below this number of semester hours.

2. The median for nonaccredited curriculums is 68 semester hours (1566 contact hours) with 93 per cent of the total clustered within 20 per cent above or below this number of semester hours.

Multipurpose curriculums

Although the foregoing sections reflect standards of technical institute curriculums which the Survey found to be generally accepted, some institutions consider the two-year pre-engineering "transfer" curriculum to be the equivalent of established technical institute curriculums. Also, some institutions try to strengthen general or vocational-trade curriculums through the addition of small injections of mathematics or science, and consider these to be the equivalent of technical institute curriculums. But it must be emphasized that neither of these expediencies produces the results contemplated by the technical institute curriculum. This issue has been confused during recent years because the great dearth of technical manpower has led to the ready employment of all graduates from any type of technical program, sometimes indiscriminately. This has led to the mistaken idea that these

TABLE 3-2

Range and Percentage of Semester Credit Hours and Median for Three Engineering Technology Areas
(Highest Frequency of "Typical" Curriculums)

Engineering technology	Semester credit hours Range	Math % Range	Math Median	Science % Range	Science Median	Major technical specialty % Range	Major technical specialty Median	Related technical specialty % Range	Related technical specialty Median	Communications % Range	Communications Median	Humanistic–Social % Range	Humanistic–Social Median	Electives % Range	Electives Median	P.E. and health % Range	P.E. and health Median
Electrical:*																	
(13) Total group	65–93	8–18	11	0–14	8	29–63	47	4–19	11	0–17	11	0–22	13	0–4	0	0–8	0
(5) ECPD group§	67–93	8–18	13	4–14	5	40–57	50	8–19	14	4–13	8	3–18	8	0–4	0	0–2	0
(5) JC group	65–78	8–15	12	0–14	9	29–63	46	4–17	4	8–14	11	11–16	13	0	:	0–8	0
(1) Pri group	91	15	:	5	:	40	:	14	:	8	:	18	:	0	:	0	:
(7) Pub group	40–93	8–18	11	4–14	8	42–57	50	6–19	10	0–17	8	0–22	8	0	:	0	:
Electronic:†																	
(27) Total group	60–91	8–22	12	0–13	10	24–80	47	0–26	6	0–12	9	0–21	8	0–23	0	0–7	3
(8) ECPD group§	60–91	9–17	13	0–12	9	27–80	57	2–26	5	1–12	7	0–12	6	0–8	0	0–4	0
(12) JC group	62–84	8–19	13	0–13	7	24–61	44	0–19	7	3–12	9	3–21	9	0–23	7	0–7	6
(10) Pri group	60–91	9–22	13	0–12	7	45–80	66	2–26	5	0–9	4	0–14	9	0	:	0–3	0
(5) Pub group	60–74	8–17	12	7–12	11	27–63	48	7–25	8	0–12	8	0–17	8	0–4	0	0–4	0
Mechanical:‡																	
(11) Total group	60–127	5–23	13	4–18	11	33–66	43	3–40	12	4–11	8	0–9	5	0–17	0	0–3	0
(3) ECPD group§	66–127	5–20	18	9–15	12	33–48	35	12–40	27	4–8	7	0–4	2	0	:	0	
(6) JC group	60–75	5–17	15	7–18	11	38–47	43	9–40	14	8–11	6	0–9	4	0–17	0	0–3	0
(3) Pri group	66–127	14–20	18	9–15	14	33–50	48	3–27	12	4–11	7	2–8	4	0	:	0	
(2) Pub group	66–70	8–9	8.5	4–9	6.5	54–66	60	7–20	14	5–6	5.5	0–8	4	0–3	1.5	0	

various approaches are equivalent to well-organized technical institute curriculums. The pay-off comes in the long-time comparative tests.

To attempt to make a dual-purpose vehicle out of the technical institute curriculum is to miss entirely the goal envisioned in the qualified engineering technician.

Summary

The true technical institute curriculum is unique in form and content. As has been illustrated previously, it serves a function not commensurate with either engineering education or vocational training.

In general, students who benefit most from the technical institute program fall into one of the following categories: (1) those who are intensely interested in a specific technological field, and (2) those who want a technological education, but who for some reason will not undertake a four- or five-year baccalaureate degree program.

It should be emphasized that these are for the most part capable individuals, many of whom simply are not interested in formal academic study toward the baccalaureate degree. For them the technical institute is *not* an *alternative* educational program. In reality, it represents the best course of study, serving a need not met by any other instructional program.

CHAPTER 4

The Technical Institute Student Body

TO EMBODY THE PHILOSOPHY and objectives of technical institute education, the technical institute must offer curriculums appropriate for the students whom it attracts.[1] This requires that the curriculums meet the occupational objectives of its students and at the same time be geared to their aptitudes, interests, and prior achievements. To supplement curriculums and instruction, there must also be appropriate programs of testing, counseling, and guidance. Furthermore, there should be appropriate provision for such services as extracurricular activities, scholarships, loans, employment placement, and housing accommodations if necessary. The purpose of this chapter is to present and discuss those characteristics of students as derived from the Survey that may assist in the design of curriculums as well as these supplementary programs and services.

Sources of students

According to Survey information for 1956–1958, the two principal groups of students enrolled in technical

[1] The term "technical institute" is used throughout this report to include all types of collegiate institutions which offer programs in technical institute education as defined.

institute programs were those coming directly from high school graduation and those coming as veterans of the armed forces.[2] The extent of these and other sources of entering students is summarized in Table 4-1. Although these data are for daytime enrollments, it may be noted that four institutes indicated 50 per cent of their student bodies came from industry. In contrast to this, forty-seven institutes indicated no student enrollment from industry. Some twenty-three institutes indicated that up to 30 per cent of their enrollment came from "other" miscellaneous sources.

The sources "industry" and "other" should not be considered unimportant. Instead, they exemplify the kind of departure from the average by which an alert technical institute may respond to local conditions and needs. Further, they represent the inevitable trend as the number of veterans declines.

In respect to each of the two principal sources of students, high schools and the armed forces, the distribution of the data in Table 4-1 suggests that during the period of the survey a large group of technical institutes had drawn heavily upon high schools for students, in some cases to the virtual exclusion of dependence on all other sources. Many institutions in this group, however, obtain signifi-

[2] Veterans of the armed forces who qualify for admission to technical institute curriculums presumably are also high school graduates or the equivalent. Yet experience and maturity acquired in military service justify classification of veterans separately from those high school graduates who have not had service experience. The veterans usually present somewhat different problems in matters such as admissions procedures and counseling, for example. The Survey made no attempt to investigate these aspects of student bodies, primarily because they arise in collegiate education generally rather than uniquely in technical institute education.

TABLE 4-1

Sources of Full-time Day Students as Reported by Ninety-seven Technical Institutes, Indicated in Terms of the Number of Schools Reporting Each Category and Percentage

Source	Percentage of student body																					Mean, %	Median, %
	0	5	10	15	20	25	30	35	40	45	50	55	60	65	70	75	80	85	90	95	100		
High school..	..	1	3	1	2	5	5	4	9	4	8	1	6	9	7	11	6	6	5	1	3	58	62
Veterans..	3	4	6	..	14	12	5	9	12	1	12	1	6	3	1							31	33
Industry..	47	19	14	5	1	2	1	1	2	..	4	..										8	3
Other....	74	9	8	1	2	..	3	..														3	2

Table 4-2

Analysis of High School Source Data (Table 4-1) Showing Distribution for Different Classes of Technical Institutes

Class of institution	N*	Percentage of total student body																					Mean, %	Median, %
		0	5	10	15	20	25	30	35	40	45	50	55	60	65	70	75	80	85	90	95	100		
ECPD	31	··	··	1	1	··	··	2	1	5	2	5	··	2	5	1	2	2	1	1	··	··	54	51
Junior colleges	37	··	··	1	··	1	2	2	··	4	··	··	1	4	4	4	6	4	··	2	1	1	64	68
Other	29	··	1	1	1	··	3	1	3	··	2	3	··	··	··	2	3	··	5	2	··	2	55	50
Total	97	··	1	3	2	1	5	5	4	9	4	8	1	6	9	7	11	6	6	5	1	3	58	62
Public	54	··	··	··	··	··	2	2	1	5	1	3	1	4	4	5	9	6	3	4	1	3	67	72
Private	43	··	1	3	2	1	3	3	3	4	3	5	··	2	5	2	2	··	3	1	··	··	46	46
Total	97	0	1	3	2	1	5	5	4	9	4	8	1	6	9	7	11	6	6	5	1	3	58	62

* Number of institutes reporting per category.

TABLE 4-3

Analysis of Veteran Source Data (Table 4-1) Showing Distribution for Different Classes of Technical Institutes

Class of institution	N*	Percentage of total student body															Mean, %	Median, %
		0	5	10	15	20	25	30	35	40	45	50	55	60	65	70		
ECPD	31	:	:	2	:	2	4	:	6	6	:	8	1	:	1	1	39	39
Junior colleges	37	1	3	3	4	11	4	3	2	3	:	:	:	2	1	:	24	21
Other	29	2	1	1	4	1	4	2	1	3	1	4	:	4	1	:	33	31
Total	97	3	4	6	8	14	12	5	9	12	1	12	1	6	3	1	31	28
Public	54	3	3	4	7	14	8	2	3	4	:	2	1	2	1	:	24	21
Private	43	:	1	2	1	:	4	3	6	8	1	10	:	4	2	1	41	31
Total	97	3	4	6	8	14	12	5	9	12	1	12	1	6	3	1	31	28

* Number of institutes reporting per category.

cant percentages from at least one other source, the armed forces. In contrast, another large group of technical institutes obtained less than half of its students from high schools and therefore was dependent upon other sources. Institutions in this latter group are more likely to be represented in the upper cluster of data for veterans of the armed forces.

Additional analyses were made of the data represented in Table 4-1 to determine if any particular type or types of institution were responsible for the tendency to fall into two clusters or groups. These analyses are shown in Tables 4-2 and 4-3 for the high school and veterans' sources, respectively. Analyses for the other two sources revealed insignificant information and therefore supplementary tabulations are not shown for them.

The subdivision of the data in Tables 4-1 and 4-3 show three subgroups of institutions that are independent of one another except for two institutions which qualify both as ECPD institutes[3] and as junior colleges. This subdivision shows clearly that there are differences between the ECPD technical institutes and the junior colleges in regard to their enrolling students directly from high schools or having students enter after service in the armed forces.

The lower sections of Tables 4-2 and 4-3 show a classification of the technical institutes in the Survey sample according to source of funds. In both tables the distribution of data for private and public institutions shows marked differences. The junior-college and public categories of institutions exhibit similar patterns of depend-

[3] An "ECPD institute" is defined as an institution of higher learning or a division of a collegiate institution which has one or more curriculums accredited by the Engineers' Council for Professional Development.

ence upon high schools and the armed forces as sources of their students. Junior colleges are not the only type of institution in the public category, but their dominant influence seems quite clear. From Table 4-2, it is quite apparent that the public institutions as a group admit most of their students directly from high schools, whereas the private institutions have been enrolling a higher proportion of veterans. In fact, it seems that the double cluster in the distribution of data for all institutions can, in the case of student sources, be attributed to the pronounced differences between public and private institutions in their relative dependence upon high schools and the armed services. No such conclusions can be derived about dependence upon industry and the "other" sources, however.

One important comment should be made about the "other" source of technical institute students. The only specific source identified more than once or twice in this miscellaneous category was engineering colleges. As might be expected, this source was productive of students for those technical institutes that were closely situated or related to a college of engineering. This type of supply could be, and in some cases is, a welcome and acceptable source, but only if students transfer as a result of good counseling based on demonstrable aptitude and genuine interest. This practice benefits students and strengthens the programs of both the technical institute and the engineering college.

Unfortunately, however, the Survey found more often than not that students who transferred from an engineering college to a technical institute were regarded by themselves and others as "flunk outs" who were not good enough to become engineers and were therefore erroneously supposed to be automatically good prospects for the technical institute. Particularly low morale among technical institute students and faculty seems to prevail (and logically so) in some multipurpose institutions, both two-year and four-year, where the members of the technical institute faculty itself have accepted the point of view that the technical institute curriculums are dumping grounds for cast-offs from the engineering curriculums. This attitude is, of course, not consistent with the concept of the engineering team. Its continued existence constitutes one facet of a major problem facing technical institute education, which is treated more fully elsewhere in this report. Because its effects tend to spread all too easily beyond campuses where it exists, this problem of widespread misconception poses a serious challenge as well as a clearly identifiable opportunity for those concerned with the recruitment of technical institute students from any source.

Characteristics of students

Survey findings revealed that one of the prominent characteristics of the technical institute student body is that most of them are composed of daytime students exclusively. There are, however, a few institutions which offer technical institute curricular programs in the evening. The number of students enrolled and the number of such programs were small in comparison with daytime programs. Though not strictly germane to engineering technician education, it should nevertheless be mentioned that many technical institutes do have evening student bodies. At some institutions, evening enrollment exceeds daytime enrollment. But, except for the very few cases as indicated, instruction given to evening students is preponderantly of the vocational-trade type. It sometimes is part of an adult education or extension program and may involve cooperation, locally or regionally, with other educational institutions. Programs of this kind also testify to the sensitivity with which the alert technical institute will detect the need for its educational service. Such response is especially noteworthy because it pertains to an educational area outside the recognized realm of technical education, an area, however, which the technical institute is well qualified to understand and serve.

The Survey collected information on three other characteristics that were of particular relevance to the nature of technical institute student bodies. These were the average age at entrance, the proportion of entering students who complete the curriculums of their choice, and the proportion of students who live in the commuting area.

The average age at entrance was reported as follows: median, 19 years, mean 20 years; range from 18 to 27 years. Of the 93 institutes reporting these data, 69 were in the 18- to 20-year bracket and 19 in the 21- to 23-year bracket.

The percentage of enrolled students reported as completing the program and graduating ranged from 5 (two institutes) to 100 (one institute). The median percentage came to 50 and the mean to 52. Twenty-nine institutes reported completions of from 5 to 40 per cent, fifty from 50 to 75 per cent, and twelve from 80 to 100 per cent. Survey information indicates the drop-out figures to be substantially influenced by students quitting school to accept jobs before graduation. In many instances such students complete the technical portion of the curriculum but do not want to wait to complete the general course requirements for graduation. This poses a problem for the technical institute in safeguarding its reputation for quality in its product.

Data submitted concerning the commuting habits of the student body revealed a range of from zero (one institution) to 100 per cent (twenty-two institutions) of students living within the commuting area. Nineteen institutions reported 45 per cent or less, sixteen reported from 50 to 75 per cent, fifty-nine reported from 80 to 100 per cent. It was obvious from reports and information submitted to the Survey that the definition of commuting area is far from standardized. In fact, this definition undoubtedly depends for the most part upon the individual student. However, an institution which gives no consideration to provision or certification of housing accommodations adjacent to its campus will usually state that all of its students live within the "commuting area."

Financial status of students

Specific information was not requested in the Survey questionnaire about the financial status of the student, but some generalized comments can be made from the information that was developed in visitation interviews.

It appears that a great number of technical institute students receive financial help from family support, scholarships, veteran status, or a combination of these.

Some students must rely upon part-time employment to help finance an education. Therefore a few technical institutes have established an employment service to help students obtain part-time employment. In a few institutes classes are not scheduled after midafternoon, thus making it possible for students to work several hours per day, in some instances a full evening shift. Some institutes, however, advise students against seeking employment during the first school year so that they may better adjust to new educational experiences and enter into social and professional activities.

Ten technical institutes were found to be cooperating with local industry in work-experience programs in which satisfactory completion was one requirement for graduation. A primary purpose of this work experience is to provide industrial orientation and practical application of classroom work on the job. Thus, close coordination between employment and classroom work is of cardinal importance. The matter of pay for the work performed in a properly coordinated cooperative work-and-school program is an incidental factor, although in many instances it is of direct importance to the student in financing his education.

Students of evening programs were, for the most part, employed full time and were pursuing their education on a part-time basis. Some institutes have scheduled part of their classes for late afternoon and early evening so an employed person might avail himself of a higher education.

Twenty-five institutions did not charge a tuition fee but charge a small registration or activity fee. Two of these were fully endowed private institutions, one in California and one in Massachusetts. Subsequently the California institution found it necessary to start charging a tuition fee. The other twenty-three were public tax-supported institutions in the community college or state-university category, one in Connecticut, seventeen in California, and five in New York. Consequently, students of these institutions have the advantage of minimum direct cost to themselves.

The philosophy and objectives of technical institute education require high school graduation, or a reasonable equivalent, as one of the entrance requirements to a technical institute program. Accordingly, this has been one of the criteria for accreditation ever since the Engineers' Council for Professional Development initiated its program for accreditation of technical institute curriculums in 1944. Consequently, a prerequisite of high school graduation, or equivalent, was one of the important criteria by which non-ECPD-accredited curriculums were judged for the purposes of this Survey.

Although the Survey did not specifically seek information on the high school subjects, if any, specifically required or recommended for enrollment in technical institute curriculums, some scattered information was volunteered. Review of this information suggests that if the student is to prepare in high school for entry into a technical institute he needs to know what the prerequisites are. Perhaps a suggested high school curriculum as "technical institute preparatory" would be just as much in order as the traditional "college preparatory" high school curriculum. At least, a definite need has arisen for the technical institute to include in its catalogue information clear statements of specific prerequisites, in terms of high school courses or possibly in terms of skills, for at least the more critical beginning courses of individual curriculums. Such practice would simplify the design of curriculums and could help in the development of a better understanding of the technical institute concept among high school teachers and counselors, applicants, parents, and industrial people. A possible supplementary practice would be to maintain courses for removal of deficiencies in prerequisites and to make it clear that the need to enroll in such courses might involve more than the advertised time for completion of the selected curriculum. Some technical institutes already are doing this. An alternate procedure would be to collect and distribute information about acceptable ways of removing deficiencies by means of summer sessions, evening classes, correspondence courses, etc., given by high schools, junior colleges, or extension divisions of four-year institutions.

Testing, guidance, and counseling

The Survey intentionally did not undertake a quantitative or descriptive evaluation of programs and procedures that are being used in technical institutes for purposes of testing, guidance, and counseling. The information sought and obtained revealed only that a variety of such programs is being conducted by a number of technical institutes. At some institutions various combinations of aptitude, interest, achievement, and placement tests are used routinely as part of the admissions process, but at others only in marginal cases. Likewise, after admission a variety of these kinds of tests is used, routinely in some institutions but in others only when individual students experience scholastic or personal difficulties.

For the past several years, discussions within the Technical Institute Division of the American Society for Engineering Education, in its sessions at the Society's annual meetings and in fall meetings of its National Committee, have strongly suggested the importance of increased attention to testing for the purposes of guidance, counseling, and development in curriculums. It is apparent that serious and continuing study is needed to achieve more precise formulation of the objectives of individual tests and overall testing programs. Also in need of more attention are the validity and reliability of tests used; construction of national, regional, and institutional norms for technical institutes; consideration of the design of special tests for technical institutes; etc. These needs stem from a growing conviction among technical institute personnel that only meager benefits result from a mere exchange of lists of standard tests in use and tabulations of cut-off scores for various purposes.

It would also seem worthwhile to explore the possibility of developing a single test that would differentiate with validity and reliability between those students who possess aptitudes for success in technical institute programs and those who possess aptitudes for success in engineering programs. The optimum basis for such differentiation would seem to be profiles determined by scores on a multisection test rather than a cut-off point on a single score. In brief, broad opportunities and stimulating challenges exist in the general area of testing in technical institute education.

Recruitment of students

Without question, the most serious general problem related to the technical institute student body is recruitment. Virtually all technical institutes have student-body capacity well beyond reported enrollments. Compounding the difficulties directly involved are misunderstanding and lack of knowledge about the nature and worth of technical institute education throughout the spectrum of society: employers, engineers in practice, engineering educators, high school teachers and counselors, high school students, parents, and colleagues and students at the collegiate level. The Survey consensus indicates, however, that there are islands in this sea of inadequate and improper understanding. The number and strength of these islands appear clearly to have grown in the past three decades, especially since World War II. From them the Survey has collected many opinions and suggestions. These have been resolved into the following brief general guide which, with local modification and adaptation, may assist technical institutes in the evaluation and development of their respective recruitment programs.

The foremost prerequisite for a successful recruitment program is "satisfied customers." That is, the technical institute must be able to show, by factual data from follow-up studies of its graduates and through outspoken—and spoken out—endorsements, that at least a few respected employers do employ and promote engineering technicians which the institution has produced. More is said on this subject in Chapter 9.

The second prerequisite for an effective recruitment program is, not too surprisingly, a competent recruitment program and team. The chief administrator of the technical institute is presumed to possess the personality, general knowledge of technical institute education, dedication, and educational and community contacts appropriate for arousing interest and enthusiasm in his institution and its program. However, by himself he cannot possibly have the time and energy to accomplish adequate recruitment. He needs at least two or three carefully selected staff or faculty members who have the personal and social traits for easily making friends and influencing people. As individual staff and faculty members may be found to perform more effectively before some kinds of audiences than others, specialization within the recruitment team is in order. Consensus is that recruitment is more effective in the long run if it is built around the objective of assistance to schools and parents in the identification and guidance of students with aptitudes and interests for careers as engineering technicians rather than the objective of crowding the technical institute with warm bodies (educational statesmanship, not proselytism).

Direct recruitment efforts naturally blend intimately with the general public relations program. Hence, local professional engineering and technical societies constitute contact areas of important potential. The alumni represent a tremendous potential and one which very few technical institutes have developed effectively.

Student services and student activities

Information given to the Survey about these two programs at technical institutes was somewhat meager. Only one comment can be made that seems at all likely to pertain significantly to technical institute education, and this is that as a group the private technical institutes seem to pay considerably less attention to student activities and services than do public technical institutes. There are exceptions in both categories to this general statement.

Perhaps the reason for this difference stems from financial considerations. Regardless of the reason, or reasons, however, the differences have two important implications. First, the emphasis upon student needs that is explicit in the philosophy and objective of technical institute education would seem to warrant serious efforts to provide opportunities for participation in activities other than study to acquire technical competence. One measure of the effectiveness of an engineering technician on the job is his willingness and ability to work in close association with fellow employees of all kinds and his capacity for leadership. For development of awareness of and competence in these facets of employment, student activities have proved to be worthwhile as a kind of learning by doing. In a broader sense, they also promote civic and social responsibility and competence. Debate continues, of course, as to how much attention can and should be given to these objectives by educational institutions in general and by technical institutes in particular.

The recruitment of students is also closely involved with the difference between public and private technical institutes in regard to these programs. Inclusion of student services and activities in the total programs should certainly not be justified as a recruitment device "to beat the competition." But acceptance of them for their value to students and community can justly be cited as evidence of genuine and comprehensive concern for students as individuals and as members of society.

Trends

Some factors relating to the general trend expected in the evolution of the technical institute student body are reflected in the following observations drawn from limited Survey responses on this subject:

1. A few institutes indicated that little or no change was anticipated, whereas others expected an increase in student numbers because of population increase.

2. A few of the more recently established technical institutes indicated plans for accommodating a 100 per cent increase in enrollment, while others were near maximum enrollment for their present facilities. Some indicated they would expand as facilities were made available; others reported no immediate plans for expansion.

3. Because of space and cost factors, many institutes indicated that a more selective admissions program will be required.

4. An increasing general awareness of local needs was indicated by a large majority of institutes. Maintaining a closer relationship with industry, high school administrators and counselors, and the general public was deemed

important and necessary if the technical institute is to serve fully the local community.

It would appear that many technical institutes are actively seeking ways and means to provide the educational services required by their communities. Continued vigilance about the attitudes and needs of the community is a prerequisite for determining and guiding the policy of a technical institute.

Evidence indicates that veterans have constituted a substantial and influential portion of the technical institute student body during the 1950s. As their number drops, the student body reverts to its normal status of being made up principally of current high school graduates. This is an important trend and, in the Survey consensus, should be encouraged constructively and aggressively if the technical institute is to develop as a paralleling and supporting alternative to the four-year engineering college. As such, it can provide effective technological education for qualified persons who otherwise can only glut the engineering colleges or remain untrained to the detriment of all concerned.

CHAPTER 5

The Technical Institute Faculty

THE TYPE OF FACULTY desired for a technical institute program is derived from the definition, philosophy, and objectives of technical institute education. Faculty characteristics may be considered to comprise two groups of attributes, one having to do with the knowledge and subject matter of engineering technologies and the other with performance of the teaching function. The latter group includes all the personality traits, the interest in students, the enthusiasm for the subject, and dedication to teaching that constitute the ideal teacher for all collegiate areas of education, not just for technical institute education. Accordingly, it is the first-mentioned group of attributes which this report will treat in the consideration given to the character of the technical institute faculty.

Within these limitations, then, the faculty (collectively speaking) for a given technical institute program should possess *and maintain up to date* the following attributes, according to Survey findings and opinions:

1. A thorough knowledge of the principles and laws of science, applied science, and engineering science directly involved in, and indirectly related to, the occupational areas for which the technical institute program aims to prepare.

2. A thorough knowledge of the topics of mathematics by which the principles and laws of science are applied in these same occupational areas.

3. Proficiency in the manual skills and use of the tools and equipment by which products, structures, and processes are produced in industry within the technologies to which the program is related; this means personal experience through professional employment.

4. The linguistic skills essential to effective communication in the relevant occupational areas; this includes use of language as a tool in human relations as well as instruction.

5. Relationships with industry by which to anticipate changes in the relevant technologies which have significance for the technical institute program; these to be developed and maintained, for example, by continuous follow-up on graduates, participation in community technical projects, membership in technical societies, summer employment in technical pursuits, subscriptions to (and reading of) professional and technical periodicals, etc.

6. Proficiency in appropriate areas of the social sciences as they pertain to practical human relations.

This list of attributes does not include knowledge of economics. However, where elements of this subject are important in specific occupational areas, it may be considered to fall within the categories of science or applied science or, as done in New York State, may be classified among "general" subjects. Rather than to introduce at this point the issue of general or liberal education and the debate which it could easily engender, the topic is omitted from the foregoing listing. Let it be understood that those technical institute programs that stress this feature will require an additional item on the list of faculty qualities. Whether a topic be "liberal" or "technical" actually depends more upon its methods and objectives than upon its name. The list of faculty qualities does not imply that each faculty member must possess all the qualities or that each item on the list refers to a separate group of instruction. Nothing has yet been said or implied about individual instructors, but rather an attempt has been made to characterize the faculty as a unit.

The problems involved in establishing the characteristics of individual instructors or types of instructors are complex and numerous. It may well be that no systematic formulation of standard specifications of this sort can be made. The more practical approach is to say that the faculty for a given technical institute program should, as a whole, possess all the qualities in good balance (judged again by the objectives of the particular program). To the administration of the program, then, rightfully falls the responsibility for periodic evaluations of the faculty in accordance with such considerations.

The foregoing conclusions may not satisfy the person who wants quick and easy rules for selection or evaluation of a technical institute faculty. It does not seem worthwhile to attempt to devise such rules. In concept, technical institute education is flexible, tied as it is to local conditions in the community and the needs of industry. In the world of today and tomorrow, a prominent feature of such conditions and needs in a given locale is change—and often rapid change. Furthermore, it is assumed as beyond debate that human beings vary widely in the combination of interests, abilities, and experience that each individual has acquired. The findings of the Survey apparently support these assertions, for a general characteristic of the information derived about faculty is the wide variation and distribution of data and opinions. This characteristic will be manifest in the following sections of this chapter which summarize findings of the Survey.

Average qualifications of faculty

As to present full-time instructors for technical institute programs, findings of the Survey indicate that estimates of the average qualifications vary in a bimodal, or two-cluster, distribution that seems to be characteristic of so many facets of technical institute education. Slightly more than half of the institutions reported that their average instructor held a master's degree (or had taken enough graduate study to be considered the equivalent). Another 35 per cent reported attainment of the bachelor's degree by the average instructor. The remainder of the institutions were about equally divided among the high school diploma, the associate degree or technical institute certificate, and an alternative of either the certificate or the bachelor's degree.

As to the part-time instructor, about the same high proportion of institutions reported that these faculty members on the average held either the bachelor's degree or the master's degree. In about 60 per cent of the institutions reporting, the average part-time instructor held *only* the bachelor's degree, while in 35 per cent of them the average full-time instructor held only a bachelor's degree. Similarly, about a quarter of the institutions reported that the average part-time instructor had earned a master's degree, in contrast to about one-half reporting a master's degree for the average full-time instructor.

Tables 5-1 and 5-2 summarize information received in the Survey on the qualifications of average full-time and part-time instructors in respect to years of experience in industry and teaching. The most obvious differences revealed are the tendencies toward more industrial experience and less teaching experience for average part-time instructors.

The summaries from which Tables 5-1 and 5-2 were derived were made independently in so far as industrial and teaching experience are concerned. They therefore do not reveal what combinations of industrial and teaching experience the average instructors in technical institute programs have had. In order to investigate this relationship, ratios of years of teaching experience to years of industrial experience, for the average full-time instructor and for the average part-time instructor, were calculated for each institution in the Survey sample for which the reported data were sufficient. For full-time instructors in eighty-six reporting institutions, the ratio of teaching experience to industrial experience ranges from zero to 5.1; the median is 1.2. For part-time instructors in fifty-seven reporting institutions, this range is from zero to 4.5; the median is 0.4.

Desirable minimum qualifications for faculty

As for both full-time and part-time instructors, nearly seven-eighths of the institutions of the Survey sample which stated desirable minimum qualifications for faculty for technical institute programs wanted the average instructor to have either a bachelor's degree or a bachelor's plus a master's degree. About 60 per cent would accept the bachelor's degree alone, while about 25 per cent wanted both.

The average minimum-experience qualifications desired by responding institutions is five years of industrial experience and no teaching experience. Most institutions would strongly desire a combination of teaching and industrial

Table 5-1

Average Number of Years Industrial Experience of Full-time and Part-time Faculty
Figures Indicate the Number of Institutions Reporting

Classification	N*	Years industrial experience											Median years
		0–1	2–4	4–5	6–7	8–9	10–11	12–13	14–15	16–17	18–19	20–24	
Full-time:													
ECPD............	27	..	2	6	5	3	6	..	2	1	2	..	8–9
Junior college......	32	..	4	7	7	1	7	3	1	1	..	1	6–7
Other............	27	..	2	11	2	4	7	1	..	..	2	..	6–7
Total........	86	..	8	24	14	8	20	4	3	2	2	1	6–7
Part-time:													
Total........	60	4	6	6	8	8	16	2	6	..	1	3	7–8

* Number of institutes reporting per category.

Table 5-2

Average Number of Years Teaching Experience for Full-time and Part-time Faculty Figures Indicate the Number of Institutions Reporting

Classification	N*	Years teaching experience											Median years
		0–1	2–4	4–5	6–7	8–9	10–11	12–13	14–15	16–17	18–19	20–24	
Full-time:													
ECPD.............	28	..	..	6	5	6	4	1	3	..	3	..	8–9
Junior college.......	32	..	1	5	1	6	8	3	5	2	..	1	10–11
Other.............	27	1	3	6	7	2	6	..	..	..	..	2	6–7
Total............	87	1	4	17	13	14	18	4	8	2	3	3	8–9
Part-time:													
Total............	58	5	19	9	11	5	4	2	3	..	..	..	4–5

* Number of institutes reporting per category.

experience, but, faced with a choice of extremes, would prefer to accept a faculty candidate having good pertinent industrial experience and "teach him to teach," rather than the reverse.

It should be recorded here that recruitment of instructors for technical institute programs has been exceedingly difficult in today's world of high demand by industry for technical personnel of all sorts. One can only speculate as to the variation in degree of influence of this situation on statements of desirable minimum qualifications for faculty for technical institute programs. It seems not at all unlikely that persons who have been directly involved in recruitment (or attempted recruitment) of instructors may have come to lower minimum requirements than if they had not been so frustrated.

In-service development programs for faculty

The importance of industrial experience for the technical institute instructors arises directly from the fundamental concept of technical institute education. In the foregoing section of this chapter the information presented indicates the high value placed upon such experience. As indicated, the consensus of the Survey reveals that in general the technical institute prefers to hire as an instructor a person who has industrial experience but no teaching experience rather than to hire one who has teaching experience but no industrial experience.

To have had industrial experience in his past will not suffice for the technical institute instructor. He must keep abreast of the new developments of equipment, materials, and procedures within his chosen technologies. The Survey did not include systematic efforts to collect detailed information on the in-service programs by which the technical institute instructor maintains contact with industry. It did confirm, however, the generally accepted fact that these programs vary widely in nature and scope.

The faculty-industry exchange seems to be one of the more effective in-service programs for technical institute faculty. It is a program which the technical institute administrator undertakes with considerable trepidation in times of manpower shortages—and understandably, for he runs the risk of losing his instructor to a better-paying job in industry. In principle, however, such programs are especially appropriate in technical institute education. They provide excellent sources of information for faculty on new industrial practices and equipment, not only while instructors are on the job, but afterward through the acquaintances he has made in industry. Likewise, the exchange teacher from industry can bring to the classroom experience and attitudes that otherwise might be difficult to provide. He may, of course, need some help in learning how to teach effectively, and in public junior or community colleges he has to clear the barrier of the teaching credential.

Demand for faculty

Serious problems in recruitment and retention of a full staff of qualified instructors were a nearly universal finding of the Survey. These problems affect virtually every aspect of the technical institute faculty, but especially quality, quantity, sources, and teaching loads. Quality, in terms of qualifications of present staffs and minimum specifications, has been treated in the foregoing section of this chapter. Sources and teaching loads will be considered in later sections. This section will deal with some aspects of supply of faculty. No attempt will be made to estimate, from the sample of institutions that participated in the Survey, how many persons are currently classified as instructors in technical institute education in the United States and Canada. The important information desirable from the Survey is the rate of increase that may be expected. Accordingly, Survey data on size of present staffs and estimates for the future were adjusted to a common basis with 1956 taken as 100. Summaries of this information appear in Table 5-3.

TABLE 5-3

Expected Growth of Technical Institute Faculties

Classification	No. of institutes	Faculty personnel reported for			Normalized indices		
		1956	1960	1965	1956	1960	1965
Private and public institutes:							
All..............	44	1168	1588	2093	100	136	179
ECPD............	20	663	848	1054	100	128	159
Junior college......	10	164	249	371	100	152	226
Others...........	14	341	491	668	100	144	196
Private institutes:							
All..............	22	702	914	1167	100	130	166
ECPD............	15	579	727	903	100	125	156
Others...........	7	123	187	262	100	152	213
Public institutes:							
All..............	22	466	674	926	100	145	199
ECPD............	5	84	121	149	100	144	178
Junior college......	10	164	249	371	100	152	226
Others...........	7	218	304	406	100	139	186

These data for full-time instructors for day classes suggest that, regardless of present inadequacies in size and quality of present faculties, there will need to be increases of approximately 36 per cent by 1960 and 79 per cent by 1965, over 1956. These increases are for all institutions. More meaningful estimates for particular types of institutions are shown in the lower parts of the tables. Some of the subdivisions involve so few data that the normalized indices cannot be considered reliable.

The principal conclusion to be derived from the Survey about future demand for technical institute faculty is that aggressive and imaginative recruitment or training of instructors will be essential. Effective ways of attracting and holding qualified instructors will have to be found. The chief source of competition for such persons will probably be, as it appears now to be, industrial firms, especially those whose operations seem most closely related to new and expanding technologies.

Sources of faculty

It has proved difficult to detect any "usual" patterns of sources of instructors for the technical institute programs included in the Survey. Some institutions have relied upon few sources, others have obtained instructors from all or nearly all known sources. Still others were between these two extremes. The pattern for those institutions drawing on a few sources likewise exhibits considerable variety in the particular sources employed. For these reasons few statistics were computed from the data on sources of faculty. Table 5-4 shows the results of the analysis that was made. These data merely show the average percentage use of each source by the various groups of institutions.

Two sources specified most frequently in the category "Other" of Table 5-4 were teacher-training institutions and retired military personnel. It was assumed that the instructors were graduates of these teacher-training insti-

TABLE 5-4

Sources of Faculty for Technical Institute Programs as Reported for 1956–1957

Classification	No. of institutes	Percentages from various sources*					
		High schools	Junior colleges	4-year institutions	Industry	Trades and professions	Other
Full-time faculty:							
All.................	80	24	7	19	34	9	7
ECPD..............	29	17	7	18	39	8	11
Junior college......	27	32	11	21	27	5	4
Others.............	26	26	2	20	33	13	7
Part-time faculty:							
All.................	58	16	5	18	40	17	4
ECPD..............	18	10	1	20	50	13	6
Junior college......	20	24	12	7	40	15	1
Others.............	20	13	0	28	30	25	4

* Designation of sources:

High schools: from high school or trade school faculties.
Junior colleges: from junior college faculties.
Four-year institutions: from college and university faculties.
Industry: from industrial organizations.
Trades and professions: from private trade, and professional sources.

79

tutions rather than faculty from them. In connection with the second group, an item of interest was a special program established to introduce and orient retired military personnel to teaching in civilian institutions.

Analysis of data on sources of faculty was not practical. Perhaps the only safe conclusion to draw from the Survey data is that all five specific sources, plus graduates of teacher-training programs and retired military personnel, have been utilized for recruitment of faculty for technical institute programs. It must then be left to each institution to discover which of these sources its recruitment program has exploited the least effectively.

Teaching loads

As Table 5-5 shows, the information submitted for the

TABLE 5-5

Percentage of Faculty Time Devoted to Instruction,
Including Preparation and Grading

Type of institute	N*	Percentage of time										
		100	95	90	85	80	75	70	65	60	55	50
ECPD.........	30	4	8	11	3	3	1					
Junior college..	33	5	4	8	6	4	1	1	4			
Other.........	27	3	6	9	2	4	2	..	..	1		
Total.......	90	12	18	28	11	11	4	1	4	1		

* Number of institutions reporting.

Survey indicates that a large proportion of the instructors in technical institute programs give nearly all their time to instruction and directly related activities. This is not to state the obvious. Rather, it should raise an important question about the opportunity these instructors have for their professional development. In keeping with the philosophy of technical institute education, these instructors should, through related study, research, or consulting work, keep themselves well informed about the new developments in the technologies about which they teach. This they cannot adequately do if such a high proportion of their total time is spent in instruction and directly related activities.

The number of hours per week that the technical institute instructor meets with his students varies widely among the institutions which comprise the Survey sample. However, the number of institutions that contributed to the scatter of data in this regard are relatively few as Table 5-6 shows. The standards for assigning teaching loads in at least half of the institutions appear reasonably similar.

Some of the institutions reported a distribution of class-contact hours for an instructor who was engaged in more than one type of instructional activity: classroom, laboratory, shop, and drawing. The clustering of the data about zero for shop and drawing activity suggests that most responding institutions had the classroom-laboratory instructor in mind.

One other bit of information relative to faculty teaching loads, namely, student-faculty ratios, is shown in Table 5-7. Use of the data in this and Table 5-6 will yield information on student-hour contact loads, which is used by some institutions as a basis for assigning teaching loads to faculty.

Table 5-7 presents a summary of Survey data on student-faculty ratios. These data are the ratios reported by participating institutions, not computation made from student enrollments and numbers of instructors. They should be used carefully and with reservation because in many in-

TABLE 5-6

Teaching Load in Class Contact Hours for Instructors Assigned Full-time to One Type (A) of Instructional Activity and for Those Assigned to More than One Type (B) of Instructional Activity

| Institutes | | | | In classroom | | In laboratory | | In shop | | In drawing laboratory | |
| Classification | Type | No. | | Range | | Range | | Range | | Range | |
				Total	Mode	Total	Mode	Total	Mode	Total	Mode
(A) Private and public institutes...........	All	59		5–32	15	11–40	20	11–33	20	11–32	20
	ECPD	18		12–28	15½	16–33	18/24	16–33	24	16–32	24
	JC	28		5–32	15	15–40	20	15–30	17/20/25	15–31	20
	Other	15		5–30	15	11–30	20	11–30	20	11–30	20
(A) Private institutes......	All	21		12–30	15	15–33	20	6–33	20/30	15–32	20/30
(A) Public institutes.......	All	38		5–32	15	11–40	20	11–30	20	11–31	20
	JC	32		5–32	15	15–40	20	15–30	17/20	17–31	20
(B) Private and public institutes...........	All	25		5–20	15	0–15	6	0–20	0	0–10	0

TABLE 5-7

Number of Students per Faculty Member

Classification	N*	Ratio								
		8	11	14	17	20	23	26	29	32 and over
ECPD..........	30	1	3	9	9	2	2	4		
Junior college.....	32	2	2	4	5	10	3	4	1	1
Other..........	30	2	5	8	3	6	2	3	1	
Total..........	92	5	10	21	17	18	7	11	2	1
Public..........	52	5	6	9	9	11	4	6	1	1
Private..........	40	..	4	12	8	7	3	5	1	
Total..........	92	5	10	21	17	18	7	11	2	1

* Number of institutes reporting per category.

stances it is found that such data are employed in ways that cannot be justified. It is legitimate for a particular institution to use its student-faculty ratio for such purposes as preparation of budgets, determination of approximate increases of the faculty for projected increases in student enrollment, and for studies of trends. When used for these purposes, this ratio presumably pertains to a particular program and its characteristics, as, for example, the pattern of class sizes, the combination of large lecture classes and small recitation classes for the typical student, and his pattern of laboratory and classroom instruction.

However, there are many limitations to the use of student-faculty ratios for making comparisons among institutions. This ratio does not reveal any information about such features as size of classes, faculty teaching loads, or quality of instruction. Consequently, the usefulness of Table 5-7 is limited. The chief justification for including it in this report is that it may suggest to the technical institute with an unusually high or low ratio (as determined from Table 5-7) that some study should be made of its practices and operations. That is, the ratio may serve to call attention to possible trends within an institution before the trends are otherwise noticed by apparently being extreme in comparison with other institutions, or, as mentioned earlier, by trends away from the usual or expected range.

Salary of faculty

Data on faculty salaries for the school year 1956–1957 were reported by only twenty-four technical institutes. The beginning annual salaries ranged from $2800 to $6300 with a mean and median at $4200. Data were not collected to indicate what previous experience these beginning faculty members possessed.

The highest salaries paid faculty members of these institutes for 1956–1957 ranged from $4500 to $8900 with a mean of $6300 and median of $6250. Insufficient evidence was available to determine whether these salaries were paid for thirty-six weeks or for as many as forty-eight weeks of instruction. However, it is known that the highest figure noted covered full annual salary including summer session.

The range of faculty salaries by type of institution is given in Table 5-8.

Information received since the Survey was completed indicates that upward adjustments ranging up to 30 per cent have been made in faculty salaries above the figures reported for 1956–1957. This may indicate some general awakening to the faculty salary situation.

TABLE 5-8

Salary Range of Technical Institute Faculty as Reported for 1956–1957

Type of institution	Number of institutions	Salary range
Proprietary technical institute.........	3	$4700–$7200
Private nonprofit technical institute....	4	3800– 6800
Public technical institute.............	2	4100– 7800
TI divisions of university or college....	6	3700– 7600
TI divisions of junior college or community college...................	9	2800– 8900
Total.........................	24	$2800–$8900

CHAPTER 6

The Technical Institute Physical Plant

As MIGHT BE EXPECTED, Survey findings indicate that the significant and sometimes subtle differences between the physical-plant facilities required for effective technical institute curriculums and those required for other curriculums are but another reflection of the difference between technical institute education and other areas of higher education. These subtle differences center in the principal objective of the technical institute—to develop a high level of proficiency in the application aspects of the fundamental principles and techniques involved in a selected area of technology.

The classroom

In the classroom, the difference may be reflected in greater emphasis upon provision for student participation rather than student audition. The use of tables instead of fixed desks or side-arm chairs provides a flexibility not otherwise attainable. A maximum area of chalkboard space adds further to the flexibility and practical workability of the technical institute classroom.

The laboratory

In the laboratory, the difference shows up—or should show up—again in ample provision for student participation rather than facilities merely for demonstration. Facilities and equipment with which the student may explore the practical application of fundamental principles and work out typical operational problems are called for. There is little justification in the typical technical institute laboratory for broad equipment of the research type including high-precision instruments or devices except in specific institutions which develop specialized laboratory technicians or sponsor technological research projects by the faculty where appropriate. There are fine lines of distinction here which merit special and particular local study with respect to specific curricular objective. In all instances the student needs to learn to use the precision instruments which he will be expected to use in industry.

The shop

Survey visitations and discussions revealed that there is general confusion about the question of the place of "shop" facilities and instruction in a truly technical institute program. In engineering curriculums of bygone years, shop facilities and shop courses played prominent roles—foundry in mechanical engineering and motor winding in electrical engineering, for example. Current trends in engineering education, however, have essentially eliminated all such topics, as engineering develops to embrace the advancing and expanding realms of science. At the other end of the technical education spectrum, in the vocational school, shop facilities and shop courses continue to play an important part—and logically so, for the development of a high level of skill and actual operating experience in the student is the major objective. In the vocational program the classroom instruction in elementary theory is auxiliary to the shop instruction and is referred to as "related subjects." This means subjects relating to and augmenting the skill-proficiency program of the shop courses.

In the technical institute program this relationship is reversed. Here, appropriate shop courses are included, where needed in the curriculums, as "related" courses augmenting and supplementing the technical subject-matter courses which comprise the core of the program. These differences may be subtle, but they are of the utmost significance in properly orienting and understanding the technical institute program, and they have a direct bearing upon the cost of establishing an educational plant and upon its effectiveness in developing qualified engineering technicians.

The library

In contrast with the vocational school, a well-organized library appropriately coordinated with the several instructional departments is a "must" for the technical institute. Ready reference to up-to-date authoritative information is the objective in a technical institute rather than an extensive research reference collection which has but limited use. For the infrequent occasion when such materials are needed, they can be found in comprehensive public, industrial, or professional libraries. Every student should be taught how to use a library and thus how to use the accumulated experiences of others.

The scope of available library materials should be broad enough to provide effective supplementary reading and references for all studies offered in the various curriculums.

This should include the general as well as the technical. Since the wealth of knowledge, in the technological areas especially, grows daily with the accumulating experiences of business, industry, and the technological professions, an appropriate range of authentic technical and professional periodicals also is basic to an effective technical institute library. The competent engineering technician needs to know how to use available literature in order to keep up with advances relating to his chosen field of technology, and to develop his potential as an effective citizen. A competent trained librarian, oriented to the educational objectives of the school, is an essential member of the faculty.

Student housing and activities

Although student housing was not a factor in the original plan and pattern of the technical institute as a localized institution, Survey findings indicate a rather definite trend toward the provision of housing as well as other student services and facilities. For example, one technical institute has bought and converted a nearby apartment house; another has bought a hotel and adapted it to provide some administrative and instructional space as well as student housing; still another provides excellent student housing and related activity facilities through contract arrangements with a nearby and well-appointed YMCA. In the comprehensive junior or community college, especially where such institution occupies a campus designed to be largely self-sufficient, the array of student activity facilities is relatively broad. The extent of such facilities is a question best decided by the individual local institution in the light of its community and educational circumstances— not to mention economics. Suffice it to say here that the subject is one which no technical institute can afford to

TABLE 6-1

A Sample of Space Allocations and Related Furniture and Equipment for Various Instructional and Related Purposes

Departments	Student capacity	Total area, sq ft	Area per student, sq ft	Value per student— furniture and equipment
Chemical technology (capacity 120):				
General chemistry laboratory.................	40	1,900	47.5	$ 525
Advanced quantitative—organic laboratory....	22	1,900	86.4	1,590
Instrumentation laboratory.................	20	720	36.0	1,250
Industrial laboratory.................	20	600	30.0	600
Electrical technology (capacity 250):				
Shop laboratory.................	18	1,560	86.7	1,390
Circuits laboratory.................	35	1,500	42.8	430
Power and industrial control laboratory........	35	3,250	92.8	3,425
Electronics laboratory.................	35	2,500	71.4	860
Mechanical and construction laboratory (capacity 250):				
Manufacturing processes laboratory...........	35	3,500	100.0	4,000
Welding and heat treating laboratory..........	18	1,200	66.6	470
Quality control laboratory.................	18	600	33.3	415
Metallurgy laboratory.................	18	750	41.7	780
Materials testing laboratory.................	18	1,050	58.3	1,560

Mechanical and fluid mechanics laboratory	18	2,100	116.7	1,280
Soils laboratory	18	1,050	58.3	389
Automotive laboratory	15	2,400	160.0	500
Surveying laboratory*	18	....	....	445
All departments:				
Physics laboratory	35	2,700	77.2	430
Drafting rooms (3) (each)	35	1,600	45.7	120
Typical classrooms (each)	35	550	15.7	18
Library:				
Reading room	75	1,800	24.0	200
Stacks (20,000 volumes)	....	1,000		
Office, work room, charge desk, etc.	....	600		
Periodical storage room	....	750		
Administrative offices	....	8,000	....	13,700 total
Student services building	....	37,000	....	45,000 total
Gymnasium	1,300	10,000		
Locker areas:				
Men	900			
Women	350			
Little theater	300			
Cafeteria and snack bar	300			

* Out of doors.

disregard without appropriate consideration in its development of educational programs.

Space and equipment requirements

Survey contacts and discussions emphasized that the function of the laboratory in the technical institute curriculum is to supplement and complement the classroom. Sufficient space and equipment to give each student a high degree of personal participation and manipulation are essential. Requirements in both space and equipment will vary widely between different subject areas. In some subject areas, the shop type of laboratory is the most effective, such as those used in some areas of the construction and metal-working technologies.

As to the general nature of space allocations and equipment requirements for different areas of instruction, the information in Table 6-1 is presented as a general reference guide. This information was furnished to the Survey by Broome Technical Community College, one of the newest in the New York State system, which was established on its own new campus at Binghamton during the course of the Survey. As this college offers several programs which are not in the fields of engineering technologies, the student service facilities are much broader in scope than would be justified by the technical program alone. Also, these general service facilities are out of line with initial operational needs because the planned addition of a future classroom building would increase the campus capacity from its initial limit of some 1100 full-time day students to about 1500. In addition to the items listed in Table 6-1, plans include the provision of a student activities room, a student store, a student lounge, and a faculty dining room in the student services building, and a parking area for approximately 500 cars.

As the Survey made no effort to explore comprehensively the matter of physical plant and equipment and hence picked up its information incidentally, the foregoing general observations represent the extent to which the subject can be treated authoritatively at this time.

CHAPTER 7

The Administrative Pattern
of the Technical Institute

THE ADMINISTRATIVE OBJECTIVE of any educational institution should be the performance of executive and operational duties so that the educational objectives of the institution may be effectively achieved. A true measure of the effectiveness of administration is determined by the extent to which the educational objectives are reached and the cost of reaching them.

Since administrative control is concerned with establishing policy and making decisions, this administrative function is achieved usually by subdivisions or departments. Basic areas of concern are instructional programs, student personnel services, business administration, finance, physical plant, educational evaluation, public relations, and student recruitment. The optimum size of the administrative staff of any institution is dependent upon several factors, such as student enrollment, the variety of instructional programs and services, and the physical size of the institution. The total scope and extent of operations usually will dictate the size of staff necessary to maintain balance. Small schools commonly are faced with the necessity of multiple-duty personnel, with an inevitable loss of administrative effectiveness and continuity.

A study of the ratio of students to administrative staff for twenty-three schools having ECPD-accredited technical institute curriculums for which information was available revealed that the ratios of ten schools tend to cluster about 50/1; the ratios of four schools tend to cluster about 100/1; and the ratios of nine tend to cluster about 150/1. The schools with the larger enrollments generally have a higher student-to-administrator ratio and therefore are less likely to be administratively top heavy.

Administrative control

Programs of instruction

The technical institute is in a unique position to offer two years of technical education to many of the thousands of young people with college aptitude who are not at present entering the four-year educational institutions. Some of these individuals lack the necessary entrance requirements for a four-year college; others lack the motivation, or, owing to other circumstances, cannot afford to attend school for four more years. A technical institute education appeals to many because it affords the individual the opportunity to work in practical and applicational engineering fields.

Development of curriculums should be dependent upon industrial needs, since industry will be the market place for the graduate engineering technician. A good curriculum will be based upon sound educational principles and geared to what industry will expect of the graduate. Continued evaluation of a curriculum is necessary because industrial processes and manpower requirements are in a continual state of flux and evolution as additional scientific knowledge becomes available for practical application. Internal academic control is of primary importance but is too often neglected. Sound techniques of occupational survey and job analysis should be used to keep curriculum content up to date and indicate where additional curriculums are needed. Advisory committees of thoughtfully selected professional and industrial people can offer valuable advice and serve as channels of contact of substantial public relations value.

Industries established during and since World War II are generally cognizant of the engineering technician and his abilities. These are presently absorbing all the engineering technicians who are being graduated by the recognized technical institutes and are training many within their own plants to help meet manpower requirements. It is possible, then, that national recruiting of the engineering technician will become as highly specialized as the recruiting of the engineer. In fact, the Survey revealed significant trends in this direction. Hence it will be of increasing importance that a curriculum be recognized nationally as an accredited curriculum. Various types of accreditation are available, but primarily of institutions. Only one agency, the Engineers' Council for Professional Development, accredits individual curriculums on the basis of appropriateness of content, adequacy of instruction, and performance of the graduate engineering technician.

Student personnel services

Personnel services for students in early technical institutes were relatively few in number because of these factors. The technical institute served a local community, and most of the students lived at home; therefore housing was not a problem. Local restaurants and cafes usually met the needs of students and faculty for noonday meals. Because of the home life of the individual student, the family doctor administered to medical needs. The technical institutes were relieved of the necessity of making these services available.

In more recent years, however, the student enrollment has come from areas other than the local community. In some institutions students are enrolled from throughout the nation and some have international students. This has placed a responsibility upon the institute to suggest housing in an inspected and approved rooming house or to provide dormitories. Because of location and the student enrollment, many institutions have also set up food services to accommodate students and faculty. Medical services are provided by medical staff in some instances or by student participation in a low cost health-insurance plan. Emergency medical service usually is available in most cities.

Most schools supplement the general course work with programs of avocational activities, social and professional organizations, and social activities. Many schools have found it necessary and sometimes advantageous to provide student loans and scholarships, to establish a cooperative work program, and to provide part-time employment service for students and a placement service for graduates.

One service which is most essential, but which in too many instances has been on a catch-as-catch-can basis, is a competent guidance and counseling service. Some schools have made ample provision for this function; others have made very little or none. Because of the higher cost of education and lack of facilities, a greater use of guidance and counseling and careful selection of students will be necessary. This will be of importance to the student, the institution, and the community.

Finance

The technical institute budget normally is divided into two parts, operating and capital improvements. Sources of revenue will depend upon the basic structure of the institution but may be derived from taxes, student fees, private capital, endowments and gifts, or some combination of these.

Reports from some institutions indicated that no expansion is contemplated, while others were reportedly in a formative period of establishing a technical institute. Industrial demand and administrative policy were cited most often as the reason for establishing an institute.

A more detailed discussion of financing will be found in Chapter 8.

Public relations

An institution seeking to be of service to the community and local industry must develop and maintain good public relations. This should include good relations with the general public and with other educational institutions as well as with industry. In a majority of cases this may require the services of a full-time worker and possibly additional staff rather than a person relieved part time from other duties.

Two-way communication between the institute and the public, the high schools, the colleges, and industry is imperative in sustaining an effective program of technical institute education.

With a decrease in veteran enrollment, the daytime institute student enrollment is composed primarily of recent high school graduates. It is necessary, therefore, that high school administrators and counselors be informed of changes and modifications that affect the institute's requirements for entering students. Very good educational relationships in this respect have been reported by institutes participating in the Survey.

It would appear that very little has been done generally to keep the lay public aware of the technical institute and the programs it offers. This is an expensive oversight for the technical institute movement.

Industrial relations are important, since industry is the market place for the engineering technician graduate, and thus consideration of what is needed and wanted by industry is necessary. Many schools have advisory committees composed of professional, industrial, and lay people, operating in separate or combined committees. The value of such a committee to an institute is dependent upon the problems and issues for which it is called upon for advice and judgment.

Diversity of institutions

The administrative patterns of the technical institutes included in this Survey are varied. The initial Survey objectives included a division of the technical institutes into five categories: publicly supported, privately endowed, and proprietary technical institutes; a division of a college or university; a division of a junior college or community college.

The privately endowed institution

The administrative organization of a representative privately endowed institution is shown in Fig. 7-1. The board of directors is composed of thirteen industrialists and businessmen plus the president of the institution. A joint advisory committee composed of four alumni and four board

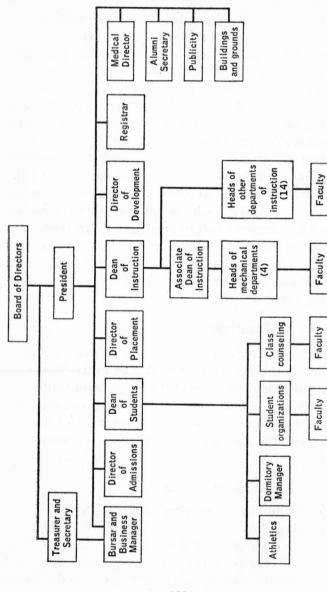

Fig. 7-1. Organizational chart of a privately endowed technical institute.

members apparently acts in an advisory capacity to the president. Administrative operation is vested in eleven individuals. Internal curriculum control is accomplished by the dean of instruction through the department heads.

This institution is not subject to external academic control, although influence in this direction is represented by the qualitative and quantitative requirements represented in the ECPD accreditation for the technical institute curriculums.

The proprietary institution

The organization chart of a representative private technical institute is given in Fig. 7-2. The board of directors

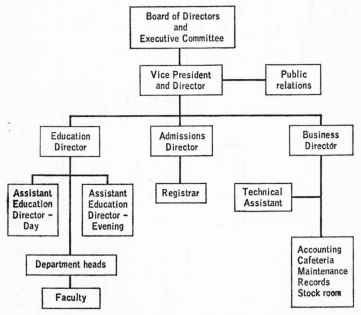

Fig. 7-2. Organizational chart of a proprietary technical institute.

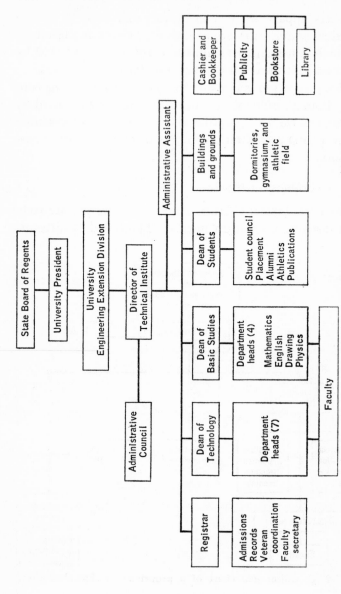

Fig. 7-3. Organizational chart of a technical institute operation as conducted by a state university.

is composed of eleven industrialists and businessmen and serves in an advisory capacity to the officers of the school. A faculty curriculum committee is used for the development and internal control of the curriculums offered. Accreditation by ECPD for technical institute curriculums, and recognition by the state department of education and by Federal agencies are measures of external academic control.

The university technical institute operation

Public. In Fig. 7-3 is shown the organization chart covering the technical institute operation of the technological unit of a state university system. Typical of this kind of situation, the board of regents is responsible for the "university system" of the state, hence it is broadly concerned with state-wide higher education and is composed of persons generally representative of business, industry, and the laity of the state. The administrative position of the technical institute operation in this instance is parallel to that of the engineering college as indicated, both being second echelon below the president's office.

Academic control is of a similar pattern. Direct responsibility for the development and supervision of curriculum content is the responsibility of the technical institute director and this is handled through a curriculum committee of faculty personnel. However, decisions as to the curriculums to be offered and other policy discussions require coordination with over-all institutional policies through the echelons indicated. The extent of this latter coordination is indicated by a board of regents decision published in 1957 to the effect that applicants for the technical institute program would thereafter be required to take the College Entrance Examination Board's scholastic aptitude tests (verbal and mathematical) as required of applicants to the institution's four-year engineering programs.

External academic controls applicable in this example include ECPD accreditation for technical institute curriculums and recognition by the regional accrediting association of the general program of the senior institution.

Private. The organizational chart in Fig. 7-4 indicates the administrative pattern for a private university. The dean of the technical institute (college of technology) reports directly to the vice-president and dean of faculties. The college of technology has the same status as other colleges of the university campus, and technical institute students participate generally in campus activities. Internal academic control of technical institute curriculums is the province and responsibility of the dean of the college of technology subject to general coordination and compatibility with general university standards. All technology curriculums are acceptable by the university as transfer credit toward a Bachelor of Applied Science degree. It is interesting to note in this connection that local industry seemed to place about the same value upon the technical institute graduate with his associate degree as it did upon the university's four-year graduate with his bachelor's degree.

External academic control of the technical institute occurs through accreditation of technical institute curriculums by ECPD and through the university's being accredited by the regional agency.

Although privately endowed and financed, this institution is also legally eligible as a public institution to receive tax aid through state junior college channels. The tax aid thus received is rebated to the student in the form of about a $5 reduction in tuition per semester hour. The dual

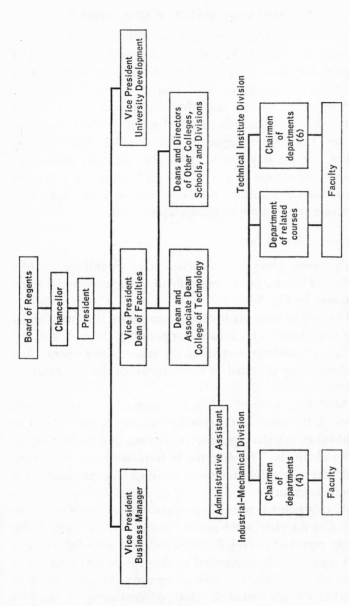

Fig. 7-4. Organizational chart of a technical institute operation as conducted by a private university.

status also introduces an element of local public control in that the membership of the self-perpetuating board of regents is subject to approval by the board of education of the local independent school district.

Another feature of the administrative program of this particular institution is its schedule of technical institute classes. Instruction begins at 7 A.M. and is completed by 1 P.M. for the day school. This class schedule allows the student to engage in part-time employment on a regular basis, and the administration conducts an active placement program to facilitate student employment.

Public technical institute

In recent years several states have established public technical institutes. An example of an organizational chart is shown in Fig. 7-5.

Control of such an institute commonly is a function of the state board of education, operating through the secondary educational system of the state. Direct operational responsibility is vested in the director of the technical institute.

Academic control of curriculums is accomplished through the usual state secondary channels, and subject to established regulations, interpretations, and evaluations of those channels. The director is responsible for local control and normally functions through the medium of a faculty committee.

At this point it seems appropriate to set down some observations which were made by the Survey staff as the direct result of Survey findings and field experiences—observations widely supported among the Survey's Regional Committee personnel across the country. This organization chart represents two of the cardinal weaknesses revealed by

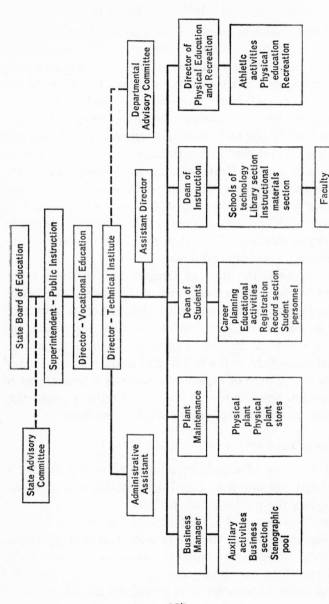

Fig. 7-5. Organizational chart of a public tax-supported technical institute.

the Survey among public technical institutes—first the tendency among public educators to classify the technical institute as secondary education instead of higher education and second, the companion fallacy of making the administration and hence the objectives and policies subservient to the department of vocational education. These are essentially the same fallacious concepts that have done such signal and continuing damage to the junior college movement in the United States. Such disservice to the American ideal of an educated youth—youth educated in keeping with individual aptitudes and interests and in keeping with the ever-advancing socioeconomic challenge —is deplorable, especially when promoted or condoned by or among professional educators.

Significantly, the state of Oregon, one of those represented by Fig. 7-5, became aware of the undesirable educational aspects of this administrative structure and took steps to correct it. By action of the 1959 legislature, the area of technical institute education in the state was removed entirely from the realm of secondary education and placed in the area of higher education as a department of the Oregon State System of Higher Education, paralleling the state university and other collegiate institutions.

Junior or community college

An example of a public community college organizational chart is shown in Fig. 7-6. This also would reasonably typify the public junior college.

The local board of education is the governing body of this institution, with the direct administrative operation delegated through the superintendent of schools to the president of the community college.

Top academic control is exercised by the state with a

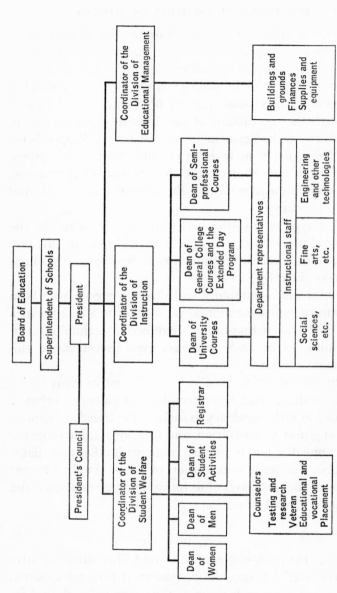

FIG. 7-6. Organizational chart of a technical institute division of a junior college.

prescribed number of academic or general subjects which must be a part of every curriculum, including the technical institute or semiprofessional curriculums which lead to the associate degree or to transfer credit. Internal control is the general responsibility of the president and is delegated through the coordinator of the division of instruction to the deans of the departments of instruction. Proposals for the development or revision of curriculums come principally from four sources: the departments of instruction, the curriculum committee, the administrative staff, and the community.

This type of institution is normally accredited by the regional accrediting association. In addition, in this particular instance, the engineering technology curriculums are accredited by ECPD.

Junior and community colleges as a group have been slow to recognize the mutual value in, or to accept the idea of, ECPD accreditation of engineering technology curriculums. As of 1958, however, some movement in this direction can be reported.

One of the serious weaknesses inherent in many of the junior colleges that are attempting to embrace technical education is the tendency to include the transfer engineering, engineering technician, and vocational-trade programs all in one division, frequently along with other miscellany. At best, this leads to confusion of the distinctly different patterns and objectives of technical institute education and trade-vocational education.

Summary

From the foregoing comments and illustrations relative to technical institute administration, it becomes apparent that there is no such thing as the "average" technical institute and no such thing as the "ideal" technical institute, except in terms of highly localized specific circumstances and conditions. What might be considered "ideal" in one community would more than likely be a misfit in another community. The "ideal" technical institute is the one wherein the technical institute idea in higher education, as discussed in the opening chapters of this report, is applied most carefully and most searchingly to meet the needs and opportunities of a given community and its related contributing area.

Likewise, the Survey findings confirm the fact that effectiveness and success in technical institute education is the product of the optimum combination of inspired and inspiring administrative leadership and competent and lucid instruction, coordinated through an appropriately designed curricular program which makes the community a part of the technical institute and vice versa.

CHAPTER 8

The Financial Structure
of the Technical Institute

THE OBJECTIVE OF THIS CHAPTER is to indicate what the general cost of technical institute education has been in the period 1956–1958 and how this education is paid for. The intention is to give a general picture of the financial pattern to be found in this area of education. The pattern is somewhat complicated by the great variety of local conditions and by the variety of types of educational institutions offering technical institute curriculums. Because of these conditions, this report is limited to the general rather than the specific in financial information in order that what is given may be considered reliable.

Source of funds

The Survey found that the percentage of school revenue derived from student tuition fees ranges from zero to 100 per cent. In 1957, there were at least two private institutions—one on the Atlantic Coast and one on the Pacific Coast—which were so completely endowed that the students paid no tuition and only small fees for incidental services. The 100 per cent free tuition factor has been maintained by limiting the enrollment to a predetermined number by means of selective tests and interviews. At the opening of the 1958 term, however, the Pacific Coast school broke with tradition and introduced a $200 annual tuition to provide funds not otherwise available for a 30 per cent upward adjustment in faculty salary level. At the other end of the spectrum, twenty institutions across the country, all of them proprietary schools, depend 100 per cent upon tuition fees. Related to this finding, the annual tuition fees were found to range from $360 to about $900 for reasonably comparable two-year curricular programs.

The Survey found 121 schools offering technical institute curriculums in 1957, and these schools indicated an enrollment totaling 47,911 in the engineering technologies. The distribution of financial support for the annual operating budget is given in Table 8-1. As reported in Chapter 1, a total of 144 schools were found to be offering curriculums of technical institute nature, but only 121 of these furnished data sufficiently complete for Survey purposes.

In New York,[1] there is a definite formula for distributing the cost of developing and operating public junior and community colleges which applies as well to those specializing in applied science or technical institute curriculums. Capital costs for establishment and development are divided equally between the state and the local community or district. Operating costs are allocated one-third to the state, one-third to the local community or district or to the county of residence of the student who comes from outside the tax district of the school, and one-third to the student body in the form of individual tuition fees. This latter

[1] Excerpts from the New York State Education Law Relating to the State University of New York, 1955, Article 126, pp. 52–61.

TABLE 8-1

Sources of Income for the Technical Institute

No.	Classification	Annual tuition fee			Source of financial support*								Enrollment
		Range	Median	% of cost†	Taxes		Private capital		Endowment		Fee and other		
					N‡	Range	N‡	Range	N‡	Range	N‡	Range	
20	Private—proprietary...	$360-$878	$701	100	0	.....	0	.....	0	.....	19	100	7,916
16	Private—endowed.....	50- 851	500	4-97	0	.....	4	3-40	12	3-96	14	4-97	7,283
8	Public—tax supported..	0- 300	281	0-33	7	67-100	0	.....	0	.....	6	0-33	3,892
13	Division of private college or university....	5- 750	281	0-100	1	12	3	5-12	5	10-100	11	0-100	6,447
18	Division of public college or university....	0- 450	95	0-100§	14	15-100	1	86	0	.....	16	5-100	9,567
46	Division of junior college	0- 600	115	0-100¶	39	0-100	2	1-10	2	2-37	29	0-100	12,806

* These columns show the source and percentage of total revenue derived from the four sources.
† This column indicates what percentage the annual tuition fee is of the total instructional cost.
‡ Number of replies.
§ Of the institutes in this category, two operate as extension programs and one as an evening program. These programs are on a self-sustaining financial basis.
¶ In this group two private junior colleges have a range from 90-100%. The range for the public junior colleges is 0-90%.

item of tuition for district residents is optional but usually applied. The alternative is for this portion of operating costs to be paid by the local district. Students from out of the state are subject to a tuition fee twice that for resident students.

In the California system of public junior or community colleges, some of which offer technical institute curriculums, no tuition fee is charged the student. Public junior colleges in California are prohibited by state law from charging tuition or fees to students within their respective districts. Consequently, the junior colleges are supported almost entirely by tax funds. Approximately half of these funds are derived from local district taxes.[2]

Instruction costs

Perhaps the most sought after and also the most elusive financial statistic and "yardstick" is the cost per student per year for technical institute education. The problem in arriving at a significant and dependable figure hinges upon semantics—definition and delimitations. The problem has been complicated in some instances by a strong reluctance to reveal true cost figures. The Survey has shown a tremendous spread and considerable carelessness or capriciousness in the use of the term "technical institute" by various schools and related groups in defining the content and objective of various curriculums. For the purpose of this discussion, the sources of cost data will be limited to those institutions having technical institute curriculums as defined and accredited by the Engineers' Council for Professional Development, plus a group of other institutions

[2] H. H. Semans, T. C. Holy, and T. R. McConnell, *A Restudy of the Needs of Higher Education in California,* State Department of Education, Sacramento, Calif., 1955, p. 51.

whose curricular offerings were adjudged by the Survey to be reasonably equivalent. These data are indicative rather than conclusive and appear in Tables 8-2 and 8-3.

TABLE 8-2

*Computed Cost of Instruction per Student per Year
in Technical Institute Curriculums*

No.	Classification	Computed cost			
		N^*	Range	Mean	Median
20	Private—proprietary.......	15	\$266–\$ 801	\$555	\$587
16	Private nonprofit, endowed .	15	182– 1100	544	420
8	Public—tax supported......	7	212– 1440	816	837
13	Division of private college or university..............	8	214– 1430	659	579
18	Division of public college or university..............	15	128– 1560	699	602
46	Division of junior college....	35	131– 1449	531	495

* Number of replies.

Another matter of some financial significance is the matter of policy and procedure in the handling of cooperative programs of part-time work and part-time study. The Survey revealed that about 10 of the 121 institutions found to be offering technical institute curriculums operate on a "co-op" basis. The general theory and ideal of the co-op plan is to provide a practical laboratory supplement to the curricular program through a specifically planned and carefully integrated employment program of work related to the objective of a specific curriculum. Although this is the ideal, the Survey revealed a disappointing degree of deviation for one local excuse or another. In too many instances, the co-op program was found to be extensively influenced

Table 8-3

Computed Cost per Contact Hour per Student for the Specified Typical Curriculum of Each Institution

No.	Classification	Contact hours				Cost per contact hour			
		N^*	Range	Median	Mean	N^*	Range	Median	Mean
20	Private—proprietary	16	1500–3960	2407	2490	16	0.32–0.73	0.54	0.57
16	Private—endowed	14	1216–2800	1836	1879	14	0.49–1.38	0.82	0.82
8	Public—tax supported	7	900–2148	1884	1770	5	0.62–1.13	0.88	0.88
13	Division of private college or university	12	404–2550	1556	1605	11	0.47–1.70	0.79	0.80
18	Division of public college or university	18	936–2916	1743	1720	13	0.36–1.53	0.67	0.67
46	Division of junior college	46	934–1928	1563	1535	26	0.36–1.71	0.76	0.81

* Number of replies.

by employment expediency. In at least one instance, the admitted objective of the co-op program was to provide the student employment to help him pay his tuition. Significantly, this same technical institute has changed its co-op program to a fully integrated educational basis with the financial aspect reduced, as it should be, to incidental status (see Chapter 4).

In at least one technical institute which possesses sound and stable programs, both economically and educationally, an approach to cost control is made on a curriculum basis. For a program of proper quality in an engineering technology, this school estimates that a minimum of 200 students must be registered in the two-year "pipe-line" of a curriculum to assure its paying its own share in the total program of the school.

Capital costs

Here again, generalizations could be more misleading than informative because of differences in local conditions and in local concepts. Hence resort is made to some representative examples reflecting dependable data. From New York, through the cooperation of Dr. L. L. Jarvie, Executive Dean for Institutes and Community Colleges of the State University of New York, and of *Technical Education News,* published by McGraw-Hill Book Company, Inc., the Survey obtained the up-to-date information reflected in the following paragraphs.

First, it should be emphasized again that several factors of local significance will affect the cost of setting up a physical plant suited to the technical institute program and the cost of operating such a program after it is set up. These factors include: the nature of the area where the institution is to be established; the nature of the curricular program to be offered; the condition, nature, and extent of the physical plant; and the number of students to be accommodated.

In New York, as of 1957–1958, there were in operation, under the supervision of the State University of New York, six "Agricultural and Technical Institutes" and eleven locally sponsored "Community Colleges." Although the specific costs vary among these institutions, experience over a period of years has led to a general formula for projecting capital costs for new construction. To develop a new campus from the ground up, the per capita cost is figured at $4000. Thus on this basis a campus fully equipped and ready to operate to accommodate 1000 students would represent a capital cost of approximately $4,000,000.

The procedure in planning buildings for a new campus is first to outline the curriculums appropriate to the location and then to determine the amount and location of space required to carry out the objectives of the educational program. At this point, the project is turned over to the architects for specific planning and design. Based upon many years of experience, a tabulation of general space requirements has been worked out and is used in general planning and design (see Table 8-4).

Operating costs

Reflecting operating costs for these institutions, Table 8-5 covers eight of the locally sponsored two-year institutions in New York which offer technical institute and other curriculums; the Agricultural and Technical Institutes were omitted from this tabulation because of the imbalance which would have been injected by the relatively high costs of programs in agriculture and the fact that these schools are completely state-supported. Actual cost per

TABLE 8-4

Standards for Determining Space Area

Space Unit	Sq Ft per Person
Faculty office	240
Instructor's office	120
Lecture room	10
Physics and chemistry laboratories	35
Laboratories (with island benches)	40
General shops (with equipment)	75
Conference room (staff)	12
Auditorium (including stage)	10
Dining space (students)	12
Dining space (staff)	20
Recreation room	50
Library	28

SOURCE: "How Much Does It Cost?" *Technical Education News*, McGraw-Hill Book Company, Inc., New York, July, 1957, p. 11.

TABLE 8-5

Operating and Capital Budgets of Locally Sponsored Two-year Institutions in New York State

School	Day enroll-ment	Oper-ating budget	Regular capital budget†
Auburn Community College*	219	$180,000	$20,000
Broome Technical Community College*	410	502,551	20,000
Erie County Technical Institute	917	665,692	50,855
Hudson Valley Technical Institute	566	381,540	20,000
Jamestown Community College*	159	187,222	36,000
Mohawk Valley Technical Institute*	524	523,781	20,000
Orange County Community College*	604	517,100	21,000
Westchester Community College*	688	504,958	14,771

* These budgets include evening and part-time costs, but the enrollments given are full time.

† Capital construction costs are not included, only annual equipment costs.

SOURCE: "How Much Does It Cost?" *Technical Education News*, McGraw-Hill Book Company, Inc., New York, July 1957, p. 11.

TABLE 8-6

Operating Budget for New York City Community College of Applied Arts and Sciences, 1947–1956, Showing Student per Capita Cost

Fiscal year	Operating budget			Total operating budget†	Student enroll-ment	Student per capita cost†
	Personal service	Em-ployer's retirement contri-bution*	Other than personal service			
1947	$ 324,867	....	$157,446	$ 482,313	1,105	$437
1948	606,720	....	188,500	795,220	2,288	348
1949	764,850	....	194,900	959,750	2,278	421
1950	830,000	....	207,550	1,037,550	2,174	477
1951	870,000	....	214,500	1,084,500	2,215	489
1952	927,140	....	228,974	1,156,114	2,257	512
1953*	1,351,088	$108,304	313,834	1,773,226	2,542	554
1954	1,228,991	149,136	229,197	1,607,324	2,543	632
1955	1,323,471	159,170	151,484	1,634,125	2,378	687
1956	1,503,288	165,225	181,092	1,849,635	2,437	758
1957	1,517,629	155,941	189,182	1,862,752	2,558	728
1958‡	1,556,122	173,409	160,347	1,889,878	2,523	749

* Prior to Sept. 1, 1953, the college operated as a state institution with the fiscal year running from Apr. 1 to Mar. 31. In September, 1953, the college passed to local sponsorship under the state's community college law, and now operates on a fiscal year running from July 1 to June 30. Thus the data for 1953 above cover the 15-month changeover period extending from Apr. 1, 1953, to June 30, 1954, and do not reflect completely accurate student enrollment and per capita cost. Prior to the changeover, retirement provisions were included in the over-all state university budget. Under the community college law, retirement is carried as a separate item in order to obtain one-third reimbursement from the state.

† This does not include a total of approximately $506,310 spent over the ten-year period for acquisition and replacement of equipment.

‡ Estimated.

SOURCE: Otto Klitgord, *Decade of Progress: Ten-year Report of the New York City Community College of Applied Science*, New York, 1957.

student was reported to range from $650 to just under $900 per year, depending upon the enrollment, type of curriculums, and the nature of plant facility.

Supplemental operating information from New York City Community College of Applied Science, a locally sponsored institution which marked its tenth anniversary in 1957, is given in Table 8-6. Much of the increase in student per capita cost is a direct reflection of the increased personnel service and improved salary schedules (Table 8-7).

TABLE 8-7

Salary Scale for New York City Community College

Title	1948	1956	1958
President.................	$9,600	$17,000	$18,000
Dean...................	7,725	12,000	14,000
Department head.........	7,100	9,960	10,360
Senior instructor..........	6,400	8,900	9,300
Instructor...............	5,300	8,000	8,000
Junior instructor..........	4,200	6,300	6,700

SOURCE: Otto Klitgord, *Decade of Progress: Ten-year Report of the New York City Community College of Applied Science*, New York, 1957.

Another example

A unique approach to the provision of physical plant facility for a technical institute is represented in the current development of a new physical plant for the "Center" at McKeesport, Pennsylvania, by The Pennsylvania State University. The University offers its programs locally at fourteen "Centers," of which McKeesport is a relatively recent development. The McKeesport building was built almost entirely with capital borrowed from local banks by a local Advisory Committee. Penn State entered into a lease-purchase agreement with the Advisory Committee and this agreement was used as collateral for the loan. The annual payments by the University are principally from student fees designed to amortize the local investment entirely over a period of years.

The cost of construction at McKeesport was reported to be about $1,000 per student on the basis of designed capacity, including moderate laboratory equipment and appropriate classrooms, library, drafting rooms, and other facilities. The building is described as of simple design and layout and devoid of "extra trimming." Also it must be borne in mind that such centers serve essentially as adjunct campuses of the University. Students enrolled there in two-year technology programs take most of their course work at the center but also attend a summer term at the main campus of the institution. To date (1958) the McKeesport Center has had only associate-degree work.

Cost control

As in any business enterprise, cost accounting and cost control are essential to the technical institute as an operating enterprise. Because the Survey interview and the financial data collected revealed room for improvement in many instances, the skeleton outline of a cost control system, especially designed for the purpose by a nationally known accounting and auditing firm, is given herewith.

Budget requests

These should originate with the head of each major instructional or operating department. They should be based upon a judicious combination of (1) accumulated past experience, (2) analysis of current trends in enrollment and related requirements, and (3) a corresponding projection of the departmental requirements through the forthcoming fiscal year. The timing of this initial action by the department head should be long enough before the end of the current fiscal year (usually about four months) to allow time for review, coordination, and administrative action to be completed and the proposed new budget to be at least tentatively approved at least a month before the beginning of the new fiscal year.

Projection of income

This should be prepared by the business manager from information supplied by each instructional department head—usually in collaboration with the curriculum control officer and/or the admissions offices—reflecting the extent and nature of student enrollment expected for the forthcoming fiscal year. This report should be prepared and submitted at the same time as the budget requests.

Monthly budget report

This is a monthly report which shows the accumulative current status against budget of (1) income by source or allocation and (2) departmental expense. With reference to expenses, it is vitally important for control purposes that a progressively current memorandum system be maintained covering commitments for expenditures beyond the current month. Then the running control figure representing the balance of uncommitted annual budget is derived by combining the current expenditures *and* the outstanding commitments.

Annual projection of departmental costs

This report should be prepared by the business manager each year immediately following administrative approval of budget requests and the projection of income. Some study will be required to determine proper bases for the equitable allocation of noninstructional expenses. Likewise, study is necessary to ascertain proper bases for the equitable allocation of any special or general income (endowments, special gifts, general fund allocations, etc.). The objective is to determine and to depict the part which each department contributes to the total fiscal picture of the institution.

Accounting procedure

The accounting and bookkeeping procedure to support the foregoing control documents can and should be relatively simple. It can be set up to accommodate the continuous inflow of items in such a manner as to minimize transferals and multiple posting and to expedite the striking off of significant totals at any time.

Survey findings and contacts confirm the fact previously known by the relatively few students of the situation—that competent technical institute education is substantially more expensive than general or nontechnological education, quality for quality. In fact, the cost is roughly similar to that for competent engineering education. The Survey finds some institutions shading the quality of their technological offerings in order to keep costs competitive or comparable with those of general education. Other institutions were found to be suffering excessive costs in technical institute curriculums because of lack of adequate cost information and cost control. Of course, in all fairness it should also be stated that the technical institute is by no means peculiar among institutions of higher learning in this respect. In any event, Survey findings and experiences indicate a general need for a much better understanding of the scope and nature of costs involved in technical institute education, for better and more specific cost data, and for cost control methods designed to enhance the educational program rather than just to balance the budget. Each institution, of course, must develop its own specific system in the light of its local conditions and program objectives.

CHAPTER 9

The Engineering Technician
and His Employment

CARDINAL IN THE PHILOSOPHY of technical institute education is the concept of the three-part "engineering team," which was discussed in Chapter 2. In turning to employment of engineering technicians, the purpose is to assess the extent to which this concept is now reflected in employment policies and practices in industry.

The engineering team—an essay of restatement

It is clear that the concept of the three-part engineering team was validated and came into prominence during World War II. As indicated in Chapter 2, however, technical institute education antedated the decade of the 1940s, actually having originated in the United States before engineering education. That is, in the beginning the function of the engineering technician was not clearly separate from the function of the engineer. One person performed, and in too many cases still performs, both functions. Failure to recognize this fact not only has interfered with proper and full recognition of the separate but intimately

related functions, but also has allowed considerable ineffi-
ciency in utilization of manpower to become a habit in
today's industrial world.

It is instructive to consider why and how technical institute education came into being so long, apparently, before
the need for it began to be appreciated. Reflection upon
this paradox brings to mind the claim of some engineers
that engineering is one of the older professions, or at
least occupations, of mankind. According to this view, the
first engineer was the man—or woman—who first supplemented his own barehanded activity with some kind of
tool that made use of the forces or materials of nature.
What seldom is fully recognized is that this same person
was in effect a one-man "engineering team"—the engineer
who had the inspiration to conceive and apply knowledge
or intuition, the engineering technician who completed
the practical application, and the craftsman who made and
used the tool. The builders who have been recognized in
history continued to embody within one person the whole
engineering team, though, as civilization progressed, master builders came into the scene and began to delegate
some of the functions of the craftsman to others. As working parties grew in size, the master builders naturally began to assume supervisory and management functions, so
perhaps in this sense business administration also should
be recognized as an old profession.

A still broader view will suggest that many builders and
master builders were more than a one-man, or part of a
two-man, engineering team. Many of them performed as
project teams, in that they also combined with their engineering and technician functions some of the functions of
architect, artist, salesman, and no doubt also of psycholo-
gist and sociologist. Still others may have doubled as phi-

losophers. Further exploration of the historical basis is not germane to this report, provided enough has been said to establish the point that, with reference to the past, one cannot talk about *the* engineering technician or *the* engineer as if each were one person who performed in a single capacity. Even in 1958 this cannot be said to apply universally. However, one result of the rapid discovery, formulation, and application of knowledge has been a continual trend toward greater specialization of manpower—that is, toward the necessary limitation of the activities of each individual to a single function or cluster of functions. Moreover, these broad categories of functions themselves have come to be subdivided in several different ways. Thus the engineering technician of today will be an electronics technician, a construction engineering technician, or a refrigeration technician, etc., while the engineer may be a research engineer, a design engineer, or a production engineer, etc.

Returning to the one-man engineering team of history, we certainly should not imply that the worker was or should have been conscious of the separate technical roles he performed. The concept of the three-part engineering team is the end result of a two-hundred-year evolution in the human mind. The necessary basis for this concept was the incorporation of modern science into engineering. In turn, modern science can claim but a few centuries of existence, since it began only after a careful observation of nature was coupled with mathematics to produce the inductive, scientific method. Only a person possessed of extraordinary vision could have foreseen that the experiments of Galileo, so hotly disputed by contemporary scientific "authorities," would provide within a few hundred years a scientific base under the activities of the master builders and thus introduce to the world the phenomenon of modern engineering.

The three-part engineering team could not logically have been recognized a half-century ago. It took the catastrophic events of World War II to abbreviate the slowly narrowing time lag between discoveries in basic science and their application in engineering. As the engineer became acutely aware of his relationship with the basic scientist, so he now has before him the conditions that bespeak recognition of his relationship with the engineering technician. That he has not fully and generally perceived this relationship is a thesis which Survey findings will support.

The demand—the ratio of engineering technicians to engineers

One way by which to judge the extent to which engineering technicians have achieved recognition in industry is to determine how many are employed per engineer. As long ago as 1928, Wickenden and Spahr[1] found evidence to suggest that, nationwide, the ratio of engineering technicians to engineers could become as much as 3 to 1 in *manufacturing* industries. Although some companies in several types of industries have achieved this or a higher ratio, the Survey revealed that nationwide the actual ratio in 1957–1958 was much smaller. The employment records of approximately ninety companies of various kinds throughout the United States yielded an over-all ratio of technicians to engineers of about 0.8 to 1.[2] This result is

[1] William E. Wickenden and Robert H. Spahr, *A Study of Technical Institutes,* Society for the Promotion of Engineering Education, Lancaster, Pa., and American Society for Engineering Education, University of Illinois, Urbana, Ill., 1931, pp. 52–60.

[2] In local regions for which data were obtained on ten or more companies, however, the local range was from 0.3 to 1.2 technicians per engineer.

the quotient of the total number of identifiable engineering technicians in all these companies divided by the total number of engineers in the same companies. The category "engineers" includes those designated as engineers by the companies on the basis of the differentiation between engineers and technicians adopted for purposes of the Survey, regardless of whether they had attained recognition by the bachelor's degree from an engineering college or by performance in lieu of this degree. Similarly, the category "engineering technicians" includes those formally trained in technical institute curriculums as well as those who by self-study and experience attained status as engineering technicians. Based only on "degree" engineers and technical institute graduates, however, the ratio of employed engineering technicians to engineers was found to be about 0.6 to 1 (for about eighty-five companies).[3]

These same data reveal that the percentage of engineering technicians which industry obtains as graduates from technical institute programs is smaller than the percentage of its engineers obtained as graduates from engineering colleges. Over-all, the ratio of "degree" engineers to "nondegree" engineers in this sample of companies is about 2.2 to 1, whereas the ratio of graduate engineering technicians to others seems to be about 1.2 to 1.[4]

These findings may tend to induce pessimism and dis-

[3] This ratio varied approximately from a low of zero to a high of five engineering technicians per engineer. (This excludes one employer of technicians who had no engineers, and for whom this ratio would consequently be infinite.)

[4] Ranges in these ratios were: For engineers, from a low of approximately 0.14 to 1 to a high of 150 to 1; for engineering technicians, from a low of 0 to 1 to a high of approximately 11 to 1. (These data exclude those for employers who had only "degree" engineers or formally trained technicians and for whom the highest ratios are therefore infinite.)

couragement among those concerned with technical institute education. That, contrariwise, they reveal great opportunities, albeit opportunities laden with challenge and necessity for hard work to achieve realization, is a conclusion suggested more strongly by analyses of other information obtained from employers that participated in the Survey. After they had given employment data on engineers and technicians, the employers were asked to estimate their current over-all ratios of technicians to engineers and to state the ratios that they would like to have "now" (i.e., 1957), five years later, and ten years later.

Information obtained on this basis from 100 companies (including a few government agencies) may be summarized as follows, the figures being the ratios of engineering technicians to engineers:

1. Group A. Composite group of 100 companies:
    Existing 1957: Range 0 to 00; mean 1.1; median 0.8.
2. Group B. 72 of the 100 companies:
    Existing 1957: Range 0 to 00; mean 1.1; median 0.8.
    Desired 1957: Range 0 to 00; mean 1.4; median 1.0.
3. Group C. 50 of the 100 companies:
    Existing 1957: Range 0 to 00; mean 1.0; median 0.7.
    Desired 1957: Range 0 to 00; mean 1.3; median 1.0.
    Desired 1962: Range 0 to 00; mean 1.8; median 1.3.
    Desired 1967: Range 0 to 00; mean 2.2; median 1.9.

The zero-to-infinity range in the ratio of engineering technician to engineers occurred because a few industries were using engineering technicians but were employing no engineers. In calculating the mean for each group, the infinite ratios were disregarded.

If the sample and all the subsamples of employers involved in the Survey are representative of the employment situation for engineering technicians throughout the country, then two conclusions are obvious. The first is that there is a current shortage of engineering technicians. Indications are that there is a current market for approximately 30 per cent more engineering technicians than are available. The second conclusion is that within the next decade employers would like to hire more than twice as many new engineering technicians as new graduate engineers, and, since they expect to hire a greater number of engineers than before, the numerical demand for engineering technicians will be greater than indicated by the foregoing ratios.

From a statistical viewpoint, it must be kept in mind that these conclusions about employment prospects are based upon data from a nationwide sampling of employers which is presumed to be a representative (i.e., random) sample of all employers. Granted this assumption, the statistics derived from the data must be understood as general rather than precise indicators.

The demand—numbers of engineering technicians

The foregoing conclusions, based on ratios of technicians to engineers, may be tested by analysis of another kind of estimates made by employers who participated in the Survey. These other estimates were expressed in terms of the actual numbers of engineering technicians employed in 1950 and 1957 and estimated to be required by 1960 and 1965. To permit comparison and analysis, these estimates were normalized for each employer by designating his estimate for 1957 as 100 per cent.[5] Straight lines were fitted (by the "least squares" method) to averages of the normal-

[5] The normalized estimates are unweighted by the sizes of the technician staffs of the various employers and are therefore appropriate for comparison with estimated ratios, which are likewise unweighted.

ized estimates. Results are shown in Fig. 9-1.[6] There it may be noted that line X indicates that the number of employed engineering technicians will increase by approximately 75 per cent for the decade ending with 1967. Line Y, however,

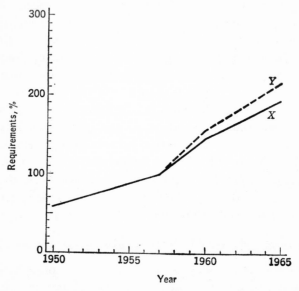

Fig. 9-1. Normalized requirements for engineering technicians (1957 = 100 per cent). Plotted points are mean values for:

   $X =$ 40 employers who employed technicians in 1950
   $Y =$ same 40 employers plus 9 others who did not employ technicians in 1950

[6] Nonlinear curves would probably have given a better fit to each of the two sets of points and might have made extrapolation beyond a few years seem reasonable. Two deterrents to the extensive computations needed to obtain such nonlinear curves were (1) lack of knowledge about continuation of existing conditions (technological, international, political, social, etc.), and (2) the limitations imposed by the nature of the basic data.

suggests that the number will almost triple. The difference between these two lines is that line *Y*, which does not extend back to 1950, takes into account nine employers who did not exist in 1950 or who for reasons of policy did not employ engineering technicians at that time.

The rather large difference in slope between lines *X* and *Y* in Fig. 9-1 means that the expected rate (9 and 18 per cent per year, respectively) of increase in the use of engineering technicians must be considerably greater for the additional nine employers than for the initial group of forty employers. However, the range is also greater for these nine employers who have begun to use technicians since 1950, and consequently it cannot be assumed a priori that a new "user" of engineering technicians will become a significant source of employment for graduates of technical institutes.[7] The general conclusion which must again be emphasized is that the statistics on future employment of engineering technicians must be considered only as general indicators of possible trends. The precautions previously mentioned should therefore be applied to interpretations of these data.

The demand—significance

From the foregoing data two important points emerge: (1) employers in general *are willing* to employ more technicians in proportion to engineers; (2) employers vary widely in regard to present practice and future plans.

Most regional committees found employers who had

[7] The ranges in indicated numbers of engineering technicians and normalized requirements for the initial group of 40 employers and the supplementary group of nine are as shown in the following table (employers A to G). To understand further the wide range of the potential market for technical institute graduates, consider the information given

never hired engineering technicians and do not intend to do so in the future. Though such employers may tempt the technical institute administrator to respond to the obvious challenge, other findings of the Survey strongly suggest that any concerted effort on challenges of this sort is far below the point of minimum return. In fact, this is the principal significance of the increasing ratios and requirements presented in the preceding figures.

Neither the data nor the opinions collected in the Survey justify the complacent conclusion that actual utilization of engineering technicians *will* automatically expand at the rates indicated. All that really can be said is that among all the employers in the country there are some who *are willing* to increase their use of engineering technicians.

by three employers, H, I, and J, whose estimates were so far beyond those of other employers that their data were not included in the computations for Fig. 9-1.

Group	Employer	Estimated requirements for engineering technicians							
		Numbers required				Normalized requirements (%)			
		1950	1957	1960	1965	1950	1957	1960	1965
40	A	1000	600	600	600	167	100	100	100
	B	80	85	90	95	94	100	106	112
	C	300	760	1500	3000	39	100	197	394
	D	40	70	140	300	57	100	200	430
	E	...	90	100	100	...	100	110	110
9	F	...	128	350	700	...	100	273	550
	G	...	2	6	11	...	100	300	550
	H	...	2	10	20	...	100	500	1000
	I	...	100	750	1000	...	100	750	1000
	J	...	4	36	96	...	100	900	2400

Perhaps a few of these would do this automatically, but Survey findings suggest very strongly that this will not hold for most, including many who may be considered to comprise the best potential employment markets. In most instances where employers were found to be making effective use of engineering technicians, Survey personnel also found that one or more nearby technical institutes had established and were maintaining strong relationships with those employers.

For optimum effectiveness such relationships should extend from the higher echelons of administration to the corresponding operating echelons, both in the employer firm or agency and in the technical institute. The relationships obviously will not be of the same frequency and nature at all levels. The contact at the operating level needs to include frequent interchange of very specific kinds of information, such as reports on operation of new equipment or processes, plans for changes in operations, performance of graduates on the job, etc. No doubt some of this information will flow through the administrative echelon (perhaps officially only here), but elaboration and discussion must go on, informally at least, in the operating echelons.

Relationships of the sort just described are not always easy to establish and maintain. Yet an unmistakable general finding of the Survey is that the stronger demands for engineering technicians exist where vigorous and imaginative efforts have succeeded in achieving first-rate recognition for the graduating engineering technician. Survey findings also imply that it is better to achieve such recognition, and to assure its persistence wherever once achieved, than to launch extensive broadcast campaigns among all local employers in a once-and-for-all "shotgun approach."

The more efficient use of limited manpower, time, and money comes from careful selection of a slowly expanding group of employers, each carefully selected as being one of the most likely local potential employers of technicians. In general, it is through such programs of coordination between technical institutes and employers that the higher ranges of ratios and requirements for engineering technicians indicated by the Survey may be realized.

Engineering technicians and engineers on the job

One of the best clues by which to gauge the effectiveness of existing utilization of engineering technicians by an employer is the attitude of supervisors and engineers of that employer toward the engineering technician and his role. Most regional committees found at least a few employers in whose firms or agencies engineering technicians were recognized and rewarded as coequal parts of the engineering team. Yet, for each employer of this sort, there were several others who did not know what engineering technicians were—or who claimed to know but sooner or later revealed an inadequate understanding or a confusion with craftsmen. The latter are not necessarily the most discouraging for a technical institute to deal with, for some of them have not yet had good opportunities to become acquainted with engineering technicians. Some of them are willing to be enlightened. The group which has fixed but erroneous ideas about the "technician" is likely to present more difficult and persistent problems. Typical of this group is the erroneous conclusion, frequently difficult to dislodge, that engineering technicians are to perform only the routine, repetitive, or distasteful jobs that engineers *can* do but don't want to do. This group tends also to regard engineering technicians as persons who aspired to be engineers but were inferior in ability and therefore reluctantly had to accept second-rate education and occupation.[8]

Though the Survey did not purposely inquire intensively into situations of this sort, some of the opinions nevertheless suggest that they result from careless evaluations of the positions and performances of engineering technicians. For example, an engineer in mid-career may be compared, by himself or his supervisors, with an engineering technician in his entry occupation. Therefore it is important in relationships with employers to be sure that engineering technicians and engineers are compared at corresponding stages in their careers.

In the early stages of his career, the engineering technician will probably work closely with and under the supervision of experienced engineers. Later he may become largely independent of the engineer or launch into a business venture of his own. Or he may remain associated with the engineer for most or all of his career. Where this happens, and where both engineering technicians and engineer progressively develop competence, the relationship can become one of mutual dependence with less emphasis on a sharp dividing line between their individual responsibilities and functions. Several examples of such a rela-

[8] Such attitudes and misunderstandings also were found among regional and national bodies of professional and technical societies of engineers. This situation represents one of the reasons for the slowness of general acceptance in the United States of the technical institute idea in higher education in spite of its long acceptance in other industrial nations. It points up also the need for better education of the general public—including professional educators as well as industry management—as to the actual dimensions of the technological manpower problem and potential and its relation to the educational pattern.

tionship were found, for instance, in representative research and development laboratories. On a given project, for example, the engineer will bring forth the initial conception of a design, general performance criteria, and broad boundary conditions of a system. The engineering technician will begin to translate these into such terms that some of the specific characteristics and operating features of the several components of the system begin to emerge. But he will not proceed independently from this stage. Repeated consultations with the engineer will occur and may involve modification of some of the initial characteristics and features. The engineer will still be in the picture beyond the stage of working drawings and construction, for he and the engineering technician can profitably continue their joint concern with the trial runs and evaluation of results.

Consider also the role that an engineering technician at mid-career or late in his career might play in the orientation and beginning stages of the professional development of the new engineering graduate on his first job. Because of the increasing emphasis that today's engineering college must place on the "science" of engineering in contrast to the "art" of its practice, the competent technician of long experience is in an excellent position to help the fledgling engineer begin to acquire the art of engineering practice that is so important in his first five years of professional development.

This is a very brief and general account, but it is by no means hypothetical, and it may serve as a general core around which the technical institute administrator can build specific examples with which to initiate and strengthen relationships with employers. By such means the administrator could capitalize upon the willingness of the more alert and progressive employers to expand their utilization of engineering technicians. By such means he could develop and achieve the beginnings of a solid recognition for engineering technicians that eventually will spread throughout the local community.

Follow-up of graduates in employment

In several sections of this chapter and elsewhere in this report, reference has been made to the effectiveness of close and continuing relationship between the technical institute and the employers in its community or service area. One of the methods which will maintain such relationships on a strong foundation and which will greatly assist the technical institute in keeping pace with the rapid changes in technology is a continuing program of follow-up of graduates. A number of successful technical institutes maintain such programs and periodically publish reports for general distribution. Aside from yielding direct benefit to the improved operation of the individual technical institute, the information collected can provide a valuable and authentic source for informing the public about the technical institute and its contributions to the community. It also can serve to focus public attention upon the good working relationship between industry and education and serve as a vehicle for public recognition and acknowledgment of such cooperation. For all these reasons, a sound, efficient program for follow-up of graduates has become an essential feature of the successful technical institute.

Opportunities for women

In all that has been said about the employment of engineering technicians, nothing has limited this employment area to males. It is true, of course, that nearly all engineering technicians employed as of 1957–1958 were men (just as it is true for engineers). Yet fundamentally there is no reason that this should continue to hold true. Studies of aptitudes found among high school students indicate that there are many girls who could become first-rate technicians in many of the fields of engineering technology. The Survey found that a few women were being educated and placed in such jobs. These facts suggest that attention to attracting qualified women students to engineering technician programs might tap a potentially large source of first-rate students and future technicians, with obvious benefits in the coming decades of shortage of technical manpower.

Employment areas

The areas of employment open to the engineering technician are as broad and varied as the areas traditionally associated with engineering and the physical sciences. The depth of penetration varies with local circumstances, but Survey findings indicate this to be growing steadily as the supply of qualified graduate engineering technicians grows and proves its productive capacity and potential. The general scope is indicated in the representative occupational titles for initial employment as recorded in Appendix 2.

A further indication of the point of entry of the technical institute graduate into professional employment is given in Tables 9-1 and 9-2. These data were developed by The Pennsylvania State University in a 1958 survey of the 1955, 1956, and 1957 graduates from its technical institute curriculums in Drafting and Design Technology and in Electrical Technology that lead to the Associate in Engineering degree. The actual occupational titles under which these 341 graduates were employed by 115 different com-

TABLE 9-1

Areas of Employment Entered by Technical Institute Graduates in Drafting and Design Technology of The Pennsylvania State University

Employment area	Graduates							
	1955		1956		1957		Total, 3 years	
	No.	%	No.	%	No.	%	No.	%
Drafting..........	6	18.2	16	31.4	49	55.6	71	41.3
Sales and service...	3	9.1	2	3.9	2	2.3	7	4.1
Design...........	22	66.6	26	51.0	25	28.4	73	42.4
Engineering.......	2	6.1	2	3.9	10	11.4	14	8.1
Research and development.......	..	...	5	9.8	2	2.3	7	4.1

TABLE 9-2

Areas of Employment Entered by Technical Institute Graduates in Electrical Technology of The Pennsylvania State University

Employment area	Graduates							
	1955		1956		1957		Total, 3 years	
	No.	%	No.	%	No.	%	No.	%
Research and development.......	5	20.8	12	21.5	18	32.2	35	25.8
Engineering.......	9	37.6	13	23.2	17	30.3	39	28.7
Production........	1	4.2	2	3.6	6	10.7	9	6.6
Electrical design....	4	16.6	12	21.5	6	10.7	22	16.2
Sales..............	4	16.6	10	17.7	6	10.7	20	14.6
Drafting...........	1	4.2	7	12.5	3	5.4	11	8.1

panies are listed in Appendix 6-A. These give a clue to the scope and nature of openings available to graduate engineering technicians across the spectrum of the various technologies.

Survey conferences and findings brought to attention the fact that in different segments of American industry there are different responses to the concept of the engineering technician. These may be classified for convenience here as follows: Segment *A*, the presently operating industries which were established prior to 1900; Segment *B*, those established prior to World War II; and Segment *C*, those which came into being out of World War II research and development. The 1958 study by The Pennsylvania State University cited previously in this chapter revealed that approximately 10 per cent of the graduates reported were employed by Segment *A* enterprises, 30 per cent by Segment *B* enterprises, and about 60 per cent by Segment *C* enterprises. This is a valuable clue for placement officers and for curriculum committees.

Salary and advancement potential

The matter of reward to the individual attainable through lifelong occupation has at least three facets meriting mention here. First, there is the self-evident but too often neglected fact that the basic reward to the individual comes from participation in a productive occupation which lies within his interests and aptitudes and which offers appropriate progressive challenge to his capacity. Another commonly neglected factor is the matter of personal "net worth," financially speaking. This is of appreciable significance to the high school graduate contemplating college. It can be shown—in fact, anyone can figure for himself from local data—that, in terms of total intervening educational costs and occupational earnings, the technical institute graduate has a long head start on the four-year baccalaureate graduate. The third facet embraces the matter of salary and opportunity for growth available to the technical institute graduate.

Survey data from ninety-two technical institutes showed starting salaries for 1956 graduates ranging from $3000 (three institutions) to $6000 (two institutions) with the median at $4520. Fifty-two of these institutions were clustered within a range of $3800 to $4500. The comparable median starting salary for four-year engineering graduates of 1956 was about $5500, according to information compiled by the Engineers Joint Council in 1958.

Placement data reported by Long Island Agricultural and Technical Institute of Farmingdale, New York, in 1956 for its 1955 graduates indicated that 100 per cent were employed, 97 per cent in the field of their schooling and 3 per cent in unrelated fields. Annual starting salaries were reported as shown in Table 9-3 by curricular fields.

TABLE 9-3

Curricular Field	Annual Starting Salary
Air Conditioning, Heating, and Refrigeration	$3380
Aircraft Operations (Base operations and maintenance)	3120
Automotive and Diesel Technology	3380
Building Construction	3800
Chemical Technology	3640
Electrical Equipment and Industrial Electronics	3380
Highway and Bridge Construction	4160
Industrial Instrumentation	3640
Mechanical Technology	3800
Technical Secretary—Industry (75 per cent women)	3380

The previously mentioned 1958 survey by The Pennsylvania State University provides the data presented in

TABLE 9-4

Salary and Advancement Record as of 1958 for Technical Institute Graduates in the Classes of 1955 to 1957 of The Pennsylvania State University

Salary	Drafting and design technology			Electrical technology		
	1955	1956	1957	1955	1956	1957
Average starting salary...	$4080	$4150	$4320	$3960	$4140	$4320
Average 1958 salary.....	5496	4900	4716	5760	5184	4680
Increase...............	34.7%	15.2%	9.2%	45.6%	25.2%	8.4%

Table 9-4 showing the salary and advancement record of associate-degree graduates of two technical institute curriculums. Salary data relating to graduate engineering technicians from Southern Technical Institute of the Georgia Institute of Technology are shown in Table 9-5.

A study of graduates from its Chemistry, Electrical, and

TABLE 9-5

Salary and Advancement Record as of 1958 for Graduates of Southern Technical Institute Chamblee, Ga.

Year of graduation	Average monthly salary			Annual salary, 1958
	Starting	1958	Increase	
1949	$238	$655	$417	$7860
1950	265	595	330	7140
1951	274	616	342	7392
1952	290	573	283	6876
1953	315	534	219	6408
1954	312	509	197	6108
1955	338	517	179	6204
1956	343	460	117	5520
1957	368	434	66	5208
1958	...	391	...	4692

Mechanical Departments made by Rochester (N.Y.) Institute of Technology during 1957 supplies the data for Table 9-6 and for Appendixes 6-B, C, and D. These tabulations provide additional insight into the growth potential available to the technical institute graduate. Data are based

TABLE 9-6

Comparison of First Jobs and 1957 Jobs for a Group of Typical Engineering Technicians Graduated 1927 to 1956 by Rochester Institute of Technology

Major occupational group*	First job		Present job	
	No.	%	No.	%
Professional (entry)...........	48	7.0	0	0.0
Professional.................	60	8.8	330	48.4
Semiprofessional.............	235	34.6	100	14.7
Managerial.................	9	1.3	96	14.1
Clerical and sales............	29	4.3	25	3.7
Skilled.....................	166	24.4	89	13.1
Semiskilled.................	52	7.6	8	1.2
Unskilled..................	22	3.2	1	0.1
Service and agriculture........	16	2.3	23	3.4
Student†...................	41	6.1	6	0.9
No job reported.............	3	0.4	3	0.4
Total....................	681	100.0	681	100.0

* The graduates have been classified according to the *Dictionary of Occupational Titles* coding. The meaning of all groups is probably clear with the possible exception of "Professional entry occupation." This has been defined as designating "persons who have the qualifications necessary for entry into work requiring the capacity to acquire and apply special knowledge involved in artistic creation, entertainment, social service work, teaching, scientific study, research, engineering, law, medicine, business relations or management."

† These numbers and percentages include only those graduates who became full-time students at some other institution immediately upon graduation and who pursued their studies to the completion of the baccalaureate degree.

upon 760 returns from questionnaires mailed to 2032 alumni who had attended or were graduated during the years 1927 through 1956.

The data collected with respect to the kinds of jobs which graduates of the institute's technical institute programs obtained upon graduation and then the succeeding movement to other jobs[9] indicate a general acceptance by industry of technical institute graduates where industry has become familiar with technical institute education. This finding is further substantiated by the salary data resulting from the study. For the composite group of 678 institute alumni who provided this information, the median salary reported rises steadily from $5623 for the group out of school for from one to five years, to $6694, $7322, $7611, $8418, and $9001, respectively, for each succeeding five-year group.

What of the future?

The career potential for the engineering technician is as broad and varied as the field of engineering itself. As with all developments in human affairs, the general realization and acceptance of this fact is evolving relatively slowly, with full measure of confusion, and against some opposition. The fact is established, however, and regardless of semantics, the trend is growing—has even grown perceptibly in strength and direction since this Survey was initiated in 1956. In substantial measure the specific extent and nature of total career opportunity depends jointly upon quality of professional performance of the present and forthcoming engineering technicians and upon the quality of educational leadership by the technical institutes which prepare and graduate them.

[9] See Appendix 6-B, C, and D.

CHAPTER 10

Problems and Potentialities
of the Technical Institute

T O A SUBSTANTIAL EXTENT, the problems and potentialities of the technical institute are indirectly reflected
throughout the several chapters of this report. Hence this.
chapter becomes a vehicle for restatement and for consideration of all relative matters as a "package" rather
than for the presentation of new ideas.

As a matter of orientation, it seems necessary to establish at the outset of this discussion that two different
aspects of the technical institute are involved. One of
these is the institutional approach—the aspect of the
technical institute as a functioning institution. The other
is the educational approach—the aspect presented by the
"technical institute idea" in higher education. In the latter case the specific institutional unit offering the technical institute instruction may be submerged as but a part
of a larger and more general institution such as a community college or a university.

Problems

Status seems to be the all-pervasive problem which
showed up in the residue of most Survey conferences:

status of the technical institute in the area of higher education; status of the graduate engineering technician; status of the whole technical institute idea in the national patterns of technological manpower and of higher education, as seen and understood—or misunderstood—by parents, prospective students, secondary and collegiate educators, professional engineers, and others including— paradoxical as it may seem—a very large segment of American industry.

The following verbatim quotation from a technical institute administrator accurately reflects a situation commonly encountered throughout the Survey:

We find that employers are eager to hire our graduates and place them in jobs suited to their knowledge and ability. Our difficulty is with the parents and the high school teachers. The latter have a tendency to advise almost everyone with average ability or better to seek admission to a university. Teachers are familiar with the recognized professions but have little knowledge of industry. Their attitude toward technical institutes therefore is regrettable but understandable.

As discussed elsewhere in this report, much confusion arises out of the fact that the word "technician" means different things to different people, both in industry and in education. Within industry the Survey found extensive confusion with respect to the engineering technician as defined. Much of this confusion arose through the chain of circumstances wherein industry, needing more technological manpower than was available through the combined output of the technical institutes and engineering colleges, has provided its own technicians by establishing and operating many internal training programs. These necessarily present highly specialized and limited content, designed to meet the need of some specific and limited phase of an individual company's production program.

Candidates for these limited plant educational programs were and are recruited in untold thousands directly from high schools and other sources such as shop and factory personnel. Those completing such training programs have to be called something to distinguish them from other categories of employees; hence such payroll titles as technicians, laboratory aides or assistants, draftsmen, engineering aides, and production assistants are formed. All such job titles apply to the graduate engineering technician, but at vastly different levels of competence, responsibility, and earned recognition. Hence confusion results when one attempts to inquire into or evaluate manpower needs or manpower utilization—confusion which merits careful and mutual efforts at clarification if the results are to be other than misleading.

Educational status

The basic question of educational status seems to stem broadly from the American tendency to regard a four-year collegiate degree as the hallmark of social establishment or distinction. This is a tendency which to date, to say the least, has not been discouraged by most of the four-year colleges or by the satellite system and attitude of most junior colleges and other "preparatory" schools. For example, there are two universities which offer certain curricular programs falling well within the "technical institute" definition of this Survey and of the Engineers' Council for Professional Development specifications, but which declined to participate in this Survey and objected to their offerings being counted or considered as technical institute curriculums. This contrasts with the fact that one of them concurrently received and accepted national recognition from another source for its technical institute program as such.

Offsetting this educational provincialism, the Survey is gratified to report the identification of several other universities of comparable quality and standing which "stand right up to be counted in public" with justifiable pride in their policy and accomplishments wherein their two-year technical institute curriculums leading to the associate degree are the equals in status and recognition of any other campus offering. In general, the findings and conferences of the Survey indicate an encouraging trend toward wider acknowledgment of the "academic respectability" of the technical institute program as defined in this Survey. The bench mark of this educational channel was the 1944 establishment by the Engineers' Council for Professional Development of inspection and accreditation procedure for technical institute curriculums. A waymark was the 1956 endorsement by the American Society for Engineering Education of the award of the associate degree for graduation from a recognized technical institute curriculum. More recently, influences in this direction have been contributed by the findings of the President's Committee on Scientists and Engineers and also by the several hundred field contacts and conferences of this Survey.

Another milestone is represented in the increasing inclusion of the technical institute type of curriculums in the rapidly expanding public two-year college. In New York State, for example, nearly 15,000 students are enrolled (1958) in this type of college, of which only some 1400 are reported to be in transfer programs. Nearly all the remainder are reported to be in the various "technical-terminal" programs, many of which are intended to produce engineering technicians and some of which are ECPD-accredited.

Although the current trend is relatively favorable in this matter of appropriate status and recognition for the technical institute idea in higher education, and although the 1958 situation may look very favorable in comparison with the near-zero status reported by Wickenden and Spahr[1] from the 1928–1929 technical institute survey, the total progress is disappointingly slow in contrast with developments in science and technology, and reflects little credit upon the American system of higher education, especially in the light of the latent capacity of that system. The burden, and the opportunity, of doing something about this naturally devolves upon the participants in and the friends of the technical institute idea in higher education (see also Chapters 1 and 2).

Professional status

Another aspect of the status problem is that of the graduate engineering technician. Survey findings emphasize the fact that there is in the industrial and professional complex of the United States no generally accepted pattern of professional recognition for the engineering technician. In this respect the medical technician, the dental technician, and various other comparable technicians in business and the professions are much better off than the graduate technician in engineering science and technology.

[1] For a more complete history of the technical institute movement, see William E. Wickenden and Robert H. Spahr, *A Study of Technical Institutes,* Society for the Promotion of Engineering Education, Lancaster, Pa., 1931, now American Society for Engineering Education, University of Illinois, Urbana, Ill.

It is the strong opinion of Survey participants in all parts of the country that this is a matter of high importance and significance. This question of status constitutes a prime challenge to leaders both in engineering education and in the engineering profession to follow the lead of the medical doctors and the dentists in helping to secure recognition for their technician teammates. Accordingly, the Survey has brought this matter to the attention of both the American Society for Engineering Education[2] and the National Society of Professional Engineers.[3] The latter body appointed a special administrative committee in 1958 to study the situation and to make recommendations. In the interim the Association of Professional Engineers of the Province of Ontario, Canada, with the cooperation of the Provincial Government, initiated in 1957 a certification program to provide a definite basis for the professional recognition of engineering technicians. In American industry the Survey findings reveal only a relatively small number of firms which thoroughly understand the technical institute idea and accordingly have the engineering technician clearly recognized and integrated into their force of technological manpower.

For every firm having such understanding, the Survey found many which did not. This situation represents either an important "problem" area, or an important "opportunity-potential" area, depending upon the attitude and point of view of approach. In any event, much re-

[2] G. Ross Henninger, "Thinking Ahead in Engineering Education: The Place of the Engineering Technician," *J. Engng. Educ.*, vol. 49, no. 2, p. 108, November, 1958.

[3] G. Ross Henninger, "Thinking Ahead in the Engineering Profession: The Place of the Engineering Technician," *Amer. Eng.*, p. 17, September, 1958.

mains to be done in the interest of effective technical institute education and the better utilization of total available technological manpower in the United States.

Confusion in terminology

What is an engineering technician? What is an engineer? What is a mechanic? One employer's "mechanic" is another's "technician." One employer's "engineering technician" may be another's "engineer." Job titles are subject to advertising's glamour treatment and to political as well as pecuniary influences.

Nomenclature might well have been the bane of this Survey—as it has been of others—except that its hazards were anticipated in the preparation and conduct of Survey field work. For example, because of the known conflicting welter of terminology involved in industrial and professional job descriptions and occupational titles, the Survey made all its industrial contacts through direct visitation and conference by pre-oriented members of Regional Committee teams. Thus the Survey, having its visitation representatives armed with its pre-established definitions (see Chapter 2), was enabled to reduce a variety of local terms to a meaningful and comparable base. Personal contact made possible a mutual understanding in terms of the manpower or job description under discussion at the specific interview.

Further clarification is needed—both in terminology and in understanding—of the boundary zones between the semiprofessional occupational area of the engineering technician and the area of the skilled craftsman and mechanic on the one hand and the occupational area of the professional engineer on the other hand. As previously discussed (see Chapter 2), these boundary zones are as important as they are confused and they are in continual state of flux. Only through a searching and correct understanding of both the interrelationships and the significant differences involved in these boundary zones can the education and utilization of engineering technicians be optimized. Only in this way can decisons and selections be made which will assure for interested American youth an appropriate education and genuine optimum opportunity for rewarding and challenging lifetime occupations in engineering and technology that will be in keeping with individual talents and interests. Here, again, Survey findings indicate an encouraging advance from the threshold reported by Wickenden and Spahr. However, this advance is not at all in keeping with the gigantic development of science and industry during the intervening thirty years. This is another "problem-opportunity" area for those interested in the technical institute idea in higher education.

The "transfer credit" question

Survey findings give rise to the observation that so long as the baccalaureate degree continues to be given the exalted social prestige accorded it by society, the question of transfer credits will continue to plague the technical institute. By definition of purpose and concept of educational opportunity, the objective inherent in the technical institute idea in higher education is to develop its students to a high level of appropriately balanced occupational proficiency in a preselected area of technological subject matter, rather than to serve as a preparatory or "feeder" school for an engineering college. As previously discussed (see Chapter 2), this singleness of purpose is described in educational jargon as a "terminal" program. Survey findings revealed that this word "terminal" has a poor connotation, causing many qualified prospective students, together with their parents and friends and even educators, to turn away from such a program in the belief that it indicates a dead-end "terminal" to educational effort or intellectual growth. Use of the adjective "occupational" instead of "terminal" would seem to avoid the negative connotation of the latter.

Survey findings reveal a preponderant—but not unanimous—sentiment among technical institute educators to the effect that a technical institute curriculum, to serve honestly and effectively its basic objective, should never be permitted to be "watered down" to meet requirements for transfer credit as that term is most commonly used in educational circles. As previously pointed out, the consensus of Survey findings is that neither the two-year pre-engineering curriculum of "transfer" institutions nor the first two years of the engineering curriculums of the recognized engineering colleges properly prepares a student to qualify as an engineering technician as defined in this Survey. The average technical institute curriculum is designed on a narrower mathematical and scientific basis than is the engineering curriculum, to enable proper emphasis to be given and proper depth of understanding to be developed in the student, within the reduced time available, to meet his needs in his selected area of technology. Hence, to enter students in technical institute curriculums for transfer purposes is unrealistic except in special and controlled circumstances.

However, Survey findings reveal what apparently is a growing tendency of engineering colleges to give advanced entrance standing to technical institute graduates in accordance with the demonstrable knowledge and proficiency of the individual applicant rather than on the basis of catalogue course numbers. This advanced standing is found to range from a half-year to two full years, depending upon local conditions and circumstances. Several technical institutes have set up specific arrangements with local colleges and universities whereby a combination of two years at each institution leads to both the associate degree and the baccalaureate degree, usually in areas other than engineering. What this really means is that in certain instances the technical institute graduate, having appropriate specialized interests and aptitudes, is recognized as a prime prospect for specific advanced work in a selected field. For example, one of the long-established technical institutes studied by the Survey has an arrangement with a neighboring university whereby a Bachelor of Fine Arts degree will be awarded the qualified graduate engineering technician for two additional years of collegiate work in communications. Similarly, a Bachelor of Education degree may be earned through two additional years of collegiate work in industrial education. There are other examples.

In any event, Survey findings and opinion indicate that the technical institute which fails to work out complete mutual understandings with neighbors among the engineering colleges and universities—to assure that its work supplements rather than duplicates—is missing an "opportunity-potential." Notwithstanding the availability of selected channels for advanced study, the prime function of a technical institute, and the principal excuse for its existence, is to develop competent engineering technicians. Everything else is secondary. There is need for a wider understanding that this is one of the various entrees to continuing education, not a dead end. The technical institute graduate, with his feet on the solid economic ground of challenging and rewarding employment in his chosen field, is a prime candidate for continuing education which is significant to his growth and development in both his occupational and his socioeconomic community.

Trend in accreditation

As the accreditation or other recognition of technical institute curriculums was zero at the time of the Wickenden and Spahr 1928–1929 "Study of Technical Institutes," any trend from that time had to be up! Nothing happened until 1944 when the Engineers' Council for Professional Development established its program for the inspection and accreditation of technical institute curriculums. By 1953, 26 institutions were listed by ECPD with a total of 76 accredited technical institute curriculums. By 1958, these numbers had grown to 36 and 116, respectively. These 1958 data break down as follows:

No. of schools	Class of school	No. of accredited curriculums
1	Comprehensive community (junior) college	8
7	Public tax-supported technical institutes	19
7	University technical institute divisions	31
10	Proprietary technical institutes	21
11	Private endowed nonprofit technical institutes	37
—		—
36		116

One of the significant aspects of the foregoing statistics is the appearance for the first time of a community (junior) college in the ECPD accreditation list. The Survey revealed that 46 junior colleges were offering curriculums of essentially equivalent nature and quality. Why the discrepancy—only one ECPD-accredited out of a potential of 46? In probing this question, the Survey revealed strong and vociferous opposition to ECPD accreditation, especially among the junior colleges affiliated with several of the self-constituted regional accrediting associations. Encouragingly, this negative attitude was not found to be unanimous.

The main difference between the two systems of accreditation is that the regional associations accredit a school and then accept *in toto* any curriculum that school wishes to offer, ranging from the classics and liberal arts to the technological or trade skill, whereas professional accrediting agencies such as ECPD will accept for accreditation only those individual curricular programs that contain content of the quality and quantity to provide acceptable competence in the selected technology area. Survey field conferences indicated an encouraging growth of understanding and acceptance of the values of this major difference in accreditation philosophy and a slowly growing recognition that each has its place. However, the Survey consensus would continue to list this as one of the "problem-opportunity" areas in which much more cooperation toward a full understanding would redound to the benefit of all concerned.

It is by no means the purpose of this Survey to "sell" the ECPD accreditation program. However, the Survey would be remiss in failing to point out the significant and strategic values for the technical institute idea in higher education which are inherent in that program. In the first place, ECPD is an independent agency built upon a joint representation from all major branches of the engineering profession. Through its functional structure of national and regional committees, it provides for a joint and balanced participation of qualified persons representing industry and education as well as the engineering profession. This provides a composite of major relevant interests, philosophies, and experiences while avoiding domination by any one. Since the engineering technician is an inseparable part of the over-all engineering-scientific-technological manpower spectrum, and since ECPD was originally established to inspect and evaluate engineering curriculums, what is more logical than ECPD evaluation of technical institute curriculums also? That the mutual values to all concerned—student, school, and employer—are steadily being more widely recognized is attested to by the growth figures cited previously.

The Survey reveals that the problem of the quasi school plagues the technical institute idea just as it does the other areas of higher education. A number of institutions were identified which called themselves "technical institutes" or which played loosely with such phrases as "vocational-technical," "technician training," or even "engineering," but whose curricular offerings failed to measure up to the minimum quality standards acceptable under the ECPD program or the definitions established for this Survey. Although it can neither be said nor inferred that non-ECPD-accredited curriculums all fall into this questionable category, it certainly can be emphasized that ECPD-accredited technical institute curriculums are *not* to be found in this category. As the engineering technician becomes more widely understood in industry, employers are found to be turning more and more to the schools having ECPD-accredited curriculums to recruit their engineering technicians. Thus this accreditation is more and more a matter of direct and serious advantage to the student and hence to the school.

Liaison with industry

The consensus of Survey participants was that close and continuous contact with industry[4] is essential both to the technical institute idea and to the individual technical institute. This close liaison between higher education and industry has been found by experience to be very important to engineering education. This is attested to, for example, by the strong and growing program of the Relations with Industry Division of the American Society for Engineering Education. This same area of mutual relationship is doubly important to the technical institute, since its basic objective is to develop in its students a high level of occupational proficiency related to current and projected needs and opportunities for technological manpower.

Survey consensus emphasizes that one of the continuing problems of the technical institute is that of keeping curricular offerings and content up to date in terms of evolving trends in technology, both in subject matter and in manpower. How else can this be done than through close and continuous liaison and interchange between schools and industry? As one technical institute president put it:

One of the biggest problems is that of maintaining continuity in the philosophy of the technical institute idea in higher education. As the era of small family industry gives way to the era of national industry and its growing branch-plant system, the nature of the technical institute's problem, both educationally and public-relations-wise, is changing. Intimacy of contact between educational institutions and local industry

[4] Here, as elsewhere in this report, the word "industry" is used to embrace the entire professional and industrial employment spectrum of the engineering technician.

thereby is becoming more difficult, and this requires and merits careful attention *plus* action.

Faculty membership in related professional societies and employer associations has been found to be one practical method of keeping up to date in any particular engineering technician field.

Other problems

Paradoxical as it may seem, in a period of acknowledged severe shortage of technological personnel in American industry, the Survey revealed that a good many technical institutes and technical institute programs in junior or senior colleges were suffering for lack of students. Contributing factors seem to be:

1. *Administrative attitude.* This was especially noted in the mixed schools where administration was oriented toward liberal arts or general education, or toward vocational or vocational-technical education.

2. *Appropriateness of curricular offering.* For successful and productive technical institute operation, curriculums must be oriented to the actual manpower needs of the community and maintained at a high level of quality.

3. *"Selling" effort.* Survey visitations and data reveal conclusively that the thriving and effectively productive technical institutes are those which augment aggressive administrative leadership and properly oriented curriculums with a strong and continuous "selling" effort.

At this point it seems interesting and pertinent for purposes of comparison to review the significant problems confronting the technical institute as reported in the Wickenden-Spahr report[5] of 1931:

[5] Wickenden and Spahr, *op. cit.,* pp. 124, 152–153, and 14.

1. *Curriculum.* The 1928 study reported that

The problem uppermost in the minds of technical-institute administrators, as evidenced by the fact that it was the one most commonly cited, was that of curriculum. That is, whether the right subject matter, in the correct proportional amounts, extending over proper periods of time, for maximum effectiveness, is being taught . . .

As of 1958, this acute problem of 1928 has been resolved to normal operating proportions through accumulating experience and development. This has been accomplished through the continuing mutual efforts of such agencies as the Curriculum Development Committee of the Technical Institute Division of the American Society for Engineering Education. Their continuing surveillance and review contribute substantially toward keeping the technical institute curriculum alive and alert to constantly evolving educational needs as well as within the scope of technical institute philosophy. That more can and should be accomplished in the development of technical institute curriculums is evidenced by the fact that ASEE is currently considering a proposal for a comprehensive study of their quantitative and qualitative requirements.

2. *Teachers.* The 1928 study reported that

Of the 12 heads of schools who supplied information, seven report no trouble in securing properly qualified instructors, two report limited difficulty, two report considerable difficulty, and one is noncommittal. The two who meet with difficulty are both heads of full-time schools of distinctive character. Their comments are, respectively, "It is more difficult than securing them for engineering college teaching" and "No source of ready-made teachers exists. Neither college teachers nor mature men from industry are satisfactory. The heads of schools, in eight out of 10 cases, prefer to obtain men from industry and to train them as needed rather than to take men already in the teaching profession."

As of 1958, this 1928 problem remains largely unchanged. In the matter of procuring the industry-oriented and experienced personnel required for competent instruction within the philosophy pattern of the technical institute, the private independent institutions and the universities enjoy an especial advantage over the "system institution." This is especially true in contrast with the junior and community colleges operating in those states which still require certification for junior college faculty along the same lines as generally applicable to the procurement and qualification of high school teachers. Such procedures operate to the practical exclusion of experienced professional technological persons in favor of graduates in educational theory. This is one of the major hurdles to be overcome if the junior or community college is to achieve legitimate status and recognition as an effective segment of higher education. Significantly, New York, Texas, and a few other states have given their junior and community colleges clear status in higher education by enabling them to emulate the universities in acquiring faculties of professionally experienced people competent in the desired subject matter.

3. *Solidarity*. The 1928 study reported that "Lack of solidarity among existing technical institutes has doubtless been a major factor in holding back the adequate development of similar schools over the country at large. . . ."

Since 1928 some noteworthy advance has been made toward "solidarity" among technical institutes and others interested in this area of education. One strong step in this direction has been the development of the Technical Institute Division of the American Society for Engineering Education. Both the Association of Land-Grant Colleges and State Universities and the National University Extension Association are giving some attention in their lower echelons to the technical institute area of education. In 1944 the National Council of Technical Schools was formed, largely by the proprietary technical institutes and related schools. The Technical Institute Accrediting Program by the Engineers' Council for Professional Development (1944) is another agency which, although not created for the purpose, is serving progressively more importantly as an area of common interest for technical institute education and as an area of mutual contact and communication between technical institute education and the engineering profession. However, as was demonstrated in the public hearings preceding Congressional adoption of the "National Defense Education Act of 1958," the technical institute idea in higher education still is far short of having an effectively coordinated channel of communication in keeping with its importance to the future of technological education in the United States. A strong and consistent voice is needed to keep the philosophy of technical institute education properly and effectively before the American public and its legislators—and its educators.

4. *Recognition*. The 1928 study reported: "The technical institutes have been handicapped by the fact that their graduates received no educational credentials which were nationally recognized. . . ."

As of 1958, this recognition problem is not so acute and universal as it was in 1928. Here, again, the 1944 establishment of the ECPD program for accrediting qualified technical institute curriculums was the first major influence toward a solution. A second major influence was the 1956 action by the American Society for Engineering Education in endorsing the granting of the associate degree in engineering or applied science for the completion of accredited two-year curriculums in engineering technologies. Thus, the 1958 trend is favorable and fairly strong toward a dissolution of the recognition problem. Continuing efforts, however, are necessary toward a better understanding among educators, the technological professions, industry, and the general public.

Potentialities of the technical institute

The potentialities of the technical institute must be considered from two angles: the educational philosophy, and the institutional aspect.

Educational aspect

So far as the technical institute idea in higher education is concerned, Survey findings suggest that the potentiality confronting it is so vast and varied as to invite use of the word "limitless." However, this idea is not generally understood or accepted. Hence the constructive development of the potential will require a continuing strong program of internal improvement in quality of program and in concert of action. In addition, a strong and consistent external public relations program aimed at a better-informed public and a better coordination of total community educational effort and objectives will be essential.

The growing need for more and better technological manpower is progressively becoming more clearly defined and more widely and clearly understood. The findings of the President's Committee on Scientists and Engineers

(1956–1958) did much to bring to public realization the fact that the much-publicized (1955–1957) "shortage of scientists and engineers" was and is actually an imbalance in both the education and the utilization of a broad range of technological manpower. This range includes scientists and engineers, of course, but also was found to include the engineering technician. Furthermore, the engineering technician was revealed to be the man actually in short supply, with resulting imbalance in the total technological manpower spectrum. Statistics from the U.S. Bureau of Labor Statistics and the U.S. Office of Education (1956) clearly reveal that not enough persons are being born to furnish through traditional educational channels the number of engineers and scientists that would be needed under existing traditional methods of designating and utilizing such manpower. This, too, reveals the scope of the present and potential need for competent engineering technicians.

Engineering is moving further and further into the realms of science in following up the ever-expanding frontiers of new scientific knowledge in contrast with the realms of application where engineering started and has grown. In effect, the engineering of yesterday, so to speak, which was the science of the day before yesterday, has become the technology of today. Similarly, today's science will become tomorrow's engineering and will become the technology of the day after tomorrow. This indicates clearly that some adequate and integrated provision must be made to continue to supply the increasing total quantity of technologically competent manpower required for this engineering application and operation and to supplement the professional engineer and scientist in research, design, and development. This manpower is supplied by the engineering technician, product of the technical institute idea in higher education.

There is significant potential for the technical institute in the socioeconomic aspect of the national manpower and educational situation. There is growing need for an educational program of collegiate level and prestige aimed at developing occupational proficiency in many areas of human endeavor between the long-acknowledged areas of manual skills or vocational trades and the purely intellectual or professional areas. This is attested to by the welter of existing miscellaneous educational efforts ranging from college extension programs to the tremendous educational programs conducted within the American industrial complex. This need is significant to the community in both social and economic terms. It is personified in the large body of young citizenry which is not being served effectively by the traditional and habitual patterns of higher education. It can be fulfilled more effectively through the technical institute idea in education, dedicated and oriented to making many more people proficient and self-reliant in keeping with their individual aptitudes and interests and yet also in keeping with community needs and civic responsibilities.

Specific potential for the technical institute is inherent in the "engineering team" concept. The technical institute can serve its community by working consistently with industries and professions to broaden the understanding, acceptance, and practical application of this concept. It can serve further by providing the necessary supporting educational leadership and the appropriate instructional programs.

Institutional aspect

The question of the status of an individual technical institute as a functional entity in a specific community, in terms of its future potentialities, is a matter about which only general observations may be made. Basically, each technical institute faces the challenging opportunities briefly indicated in the opening section of this chapter and elsewhere throughout this report. However, Survey findings indicate that what can or may develop in any individual instance is inescapably and very largely the product of purely local personalities, leadership, and conditions. Although this obviously is not peculiar to the technical institute, it is evident that the technical institute is particularly sensitive to these circumstances.

The institutional aspect of the future potentiality of the technical institute idea in higher education is harder to pin down specifically (see also Chapter 2). According to Survey consensus, the fundamental and vital point is qualitative rather than quantitative. It is the concept that technical institute education as defined is inseparably an area of higher education and intimately related to the area of engineering education. The engineering technician is an inseparable part of the national technological manpower spectrum along with the professional engineers and scientists. Prerequisites for success as an engineering technician, both in personal attributes and in secondary educational preparation, closely parallel those required for success in engineering. Institutionally, the area of greatest confusion on this point is revealed to be the area of public tax-supported education.

Hence, Survey consensus emphasizes that any school presuming to produce graduates qualified for recognition as engineering technicians must of necessity be qualified to operate—and must operate—as an element in the system of higher education rather than as any part of the secondary system or of the various less-than-college-grade vocational-trade, vocational-industrial, or vocational-technical systems found in most states.

Survey findings indicate the university or engineering college to be in a strategic and logical position in the educational spectrum to foster or sponsor the area of technical institute education. As is common in matters of human concern, opinions vary on this point. However, the Survey findings do list strong and effective patterns of ECPD-accredited technical institute education under university surveillance, such as Georgia Institute of Technology, Oklahoma State University, the University of Dayton, and the University of Houston, all of which conduct the programs on their main campuses; Purdue University, The Pennsylvania State University, and the State University of New York, each of which conducts the program through a state-wide system of campuses. During the course of the Survey the University of North Carolina placed in operation the first unit of a proposed state-wide system of technical institutes.

In Oregon and in Connecticut, state-supported technical institutes have been developed to a quality achieving accreditation by the Engineers' Council for Professional Development. These have operated under the surveillance of the vocational departments of the state boards of public instruction. However, at least in Oregon, a strong movement in the state legislature has been successful in transferring Oregon Technical Institute to the Oregon State

System of Higher Education as a separate and distinct department and an integral part of the system.

The junior and community college in the pattern of education beyond the high school also holds considerable potential for technical institute education. It must be emphasized, however, that this potential is in large measure distinctly in the future and that its effective development depends upon some effective reorientation of traditional concept and philosophy. With some notable exceptions, Survey findings reveal that most of the approximately 650 junior and community colleges of the United States are dedicated to or preoccupied with preparatory programs designed for college transfer and these preponderantly in the field of liberal arts or "general" subject matter. From this academic extreme, many of these schools jump to the opposite extreme of vocational and shop courses featuring the development of manual skills. Most such schools have left untouched the intervening area of curriculums designed to develop occupational proficiency in the engineering and related technologies. In some instances there have been casual and ineffective attempts to serve this area by modifying general curriculums or shop courses through the injection of some scattered courses in science and mathematics.

Analysis of Survey data reveals, however, some forty-six institutions in the junior or community college category that are doing significant work in the area of technical institute education. Of these, one has curriculums accredited by ECPD and the remainder probably could qualify if they were interested and authorized. Even so, and making further allowances for the fact that technical institute education is not necessarily a logical or productive enterprise for every junior or community college, the future potential of this class of institution is considerable and of especial significance in view of the "tidal wave" of students expected at the college level during the next decade.

The potential for the future of the private independent institution, either proprietary or endowed, in the area of technical institute education is really a crystal-gazing question which defies anything but conditional predictions. As a class, the private institution enjoys a position of strength in its flexibility and ready adaptability to changing educational requirements and opportunities. This is in contrast to the inertial and leveling effect of any large system or of an institutional affiliation such as might be represented in a department of a university. Capitalization upon such attributes as this flexibility and relative freedom of action is directly contingent upon the competence and initiative of administration and faculty and upon the quality and quantity of local community and industrial contact and mutual understanding. Thus, whereas any institution is sensitive to its leadership, the private independent technical institute is especially sensitive. It has no system within which to coast along and it may be confronted with direct and stiff competition from public tax-supported institutions. In fact, the independent technical institutes of the United States face some uncertain prospects in this direction under the provisions of the National Defense Education Act of 1958, which unhappily confuses the "area vocational school" idea with technical institute education.

It is interesting and pertinent at this point to quote from the Wickenden-Spahr 1928 study[6] of technical institute education:

[6] Wickenden and Spahr, *op. cit.*, p. 13.

The function of the independent, endowed technical institute resembles that of the endowed college or university in many respects. It has been almost a rule in American experience that private initiative has been quicker to recognize neglected areas of education and to occupy them than public authorities. At a later stage, after the need has been advertised and examples of successful effort have gained some prominence, the public steps in and meets the larger needs. The independent schools are then able to capitalize their freedom for experimentation with curricula, teaching methods, and selective standards of admission, and to strive toward ideals of special excellence rather than the largest enrollments or most inclusive service. The private proprietary institution has been able to maintain itself in this field because of needs otherwise unprovided for. . . . Doubtless there will always be a place for highly distinctive schools of this character, but the future of self-financing schools is highly precarious. . . .

These observations originating in 1928 are applicable in 1959. As of 1959, however, the much-publicized impending "tidal wave" of college-age youth, as it impinges upon established tax-supported collegiate institutions, seems likely to create an economic supply-versus-demand situation in which the competent, alert, and aggressive private institution may continue to survive and serve its community. It is not enough, however, that such institutions do the obvious in developing and offering a "better mousetrap" in technological education intimately geared to the needs of their communities. This is a "selling age," and this educational commodity has to be sold just as aggressively and intelligently as any other product. Further, the social as well as the economic value to both the individual and the community must be self-evident in the quality and performance of the graduate.

Summary

The problems confronting the technical institute may be summarized by listing most of those common to other areas of higher education plus a few special ones such as status and recognition. Also, for the different classes of institutions there are problems peculiar to the class.

The opportunity confronting the technical institute may be summarized by saying that the technical institute idea in higher education offers a well-pioneered educational pattern and philosophy through which a higher proportion of American youth can be brought to a productive realization of their ambitions in keeping with their individual interests and aptitudes.

Appendix 1. Participation in field survey

The field program of the Survey was conducted through fourteen Regional Committees strategically centered throughout the United States. Each of these groups worked to a standard pattern established for the Survey, but each was charged with the responsibility of making full use of its knowledge and understanding of educational and industrial conditions prevalent in its region.

The scope and success of the Survey must be credited to these people and to the support given to them in this project by their employers. In the direct pursuit of this assignment in public service to education, the 143 people named in the listings of Appendix 1-A following contributed a total of more than 753 days of time and traveled a total of at least 125,182 man-miles. These people, normally operating in teams of two, visited and conducted interviews at 90 educational institutions in 39 states and 140 industrial enterprises or other employers of technological personnel in 25 states. These visits also included schools and industries in the State of Nuevo León, Mexico, and the Provinces of Ontario and Manitoba. They were generously aided by the people at the schools and industries visited.

A. Regional Committee Personnel

REGION I

MacKenzie, Donald H., *Chairman,* Northeastern University, Boston

Libby, Douglas F., Jr., *Co-chairman,* Wentworth Institute, Boston

Dantona, Leo Robert, The Franklin Institute, Boston
Dunphy, Philip W., Northeastern University, Boston
Elberfeld, John, Worcester Junior College, Worcester, Mass.
Fellows, Douglas M., The Ward School of Electronics, University of Hartford, Hartford, Conn.
Hesselschwerdt, August L., Jr., Massachusetts Institute of Technology, Cambridge, Mass.
Keating, Arthur E., Bridgeport Engineering Institute, Bridgeport, Conn.
Van Dusen, Edward B., Wentworth Institute, Boston

REGION II

Tyrrell, Cecil C., *Chairman,* Broome Technical Community College, Binghamton, N.Y.
Notar, Ernest, *Co-chairman,* Erie County Technical Institute, Buffalo
Kassidy, Harry, Erie County Technical Institute, Buffalo
Smith, Leo F., Rochester Institute of Technology, Rochester, N.Y.

REGION III

Martin, Philip C., *Chairman,* Westchester Community College, White Plains, N.Y.
Laffin, Charles W., Jr., *Vice-chairman,* New York City Community College, Brooklyn, N.Y.
Anderson, Charles R., Pratt Institute, Brooklyn, N.Y.
Coder, Charles H., Jr., Academy of Aeronautics, Flushing, N.Y.
Desnoyers, Harold B., Westchester Community College, White Plains, N.Y.
Fezer, Harold, RCA Institutes, Inc., New York
Fibel, Lewis R., New York City Community College, Brooklyn, N.Y.
Hartung, Walter M., Academy of Aeronautics, Flushing, N.Y.
Maedel, George F., RCA Institutes, Inc., New York
McKeown, John W., RCA Institutes, Inc., New York
Zelios, Demetrius, Pratt Institute, Brooklyn, N.Y.

Advisory

Booher, Edward E., McGraw-Hill Book Company, Inc., New York

Delgrosso, Angelo L., Westchester Community College, White Plains, N.Y.

Doll, Alfred W., Pratt Institute, Brooklyn, N.Y.

Jarvie, Lawrence L., State University of New York, Albany, N.Y.

REGION IV

Fischer, Floyd B., *Chairman,* The Pennsylvania State University, University Park, Pa.

McCord, Robert E., *Vice-chairman,* The Pennsylvania State University, University Park, Pa.

Deyo, Donald E., Montgomery Junior College, Takoma Park, Md.

Dickinson, Walter P., The Pennsylvania State University Center, Wilkes-Barre, Pa.

Dimasi, Louis A., Penn Technical Institute, Pittsburgh

Helffrich, Randolph G., Spring Garden Institute, Philadelphia

Layton, Harry S., Rutgers University, New Brunswick, N.J.

Moore, Frank B., The Pennsylvania State University, University Park, Pa.

Whipple, Walter G., Westinghouse Electric Corporation, East Pittsburgh, Pa.

REGION V

Hunt, Donald C., *Chairman,* University of Detroit, Detroit

Flarity, Earl C., *Co-chairman,* Chrysler Corporation, Highland Park, Mich.

Budde, Francis J., Ford Motor Company, Dearborn, Mich.

Darling, Raymond O., General Motors Technical Center, Detroit

Freund, C. J., University of Detroit, Detroit

Hellwarth, A. R., Detroit Edison Company, Detroit

Jacobs, Paul G., Vinco Corporation, Detroit

Sehn, William E., Fisher Body Division, General Motors Corporation, Detroit

REGION VI

Csaszar, Paul V., *Chairman,* International Business Machines Corporation, Hammond, Ind.

Burroughs, Kenneth L., *Co-chairman,* Aeronautical University, Chicago

Morey, Leslie G., *Co-chairman,* Chicago Technical College, Chicago

Crakes, C. R., DeVry Technical Institute, Chicago

Elliott, Carl H., Socony Mobil Oil Company, East Chicago, Ind.

Haubrich, Joseph A., International Business Machines Corporation, Chicago

Heath, Harold, Western Electric Company, Chicago

Kuschel, W. G., International Business Machines Corporation, Chicago

Lafeber, T. J., DeVry Technical Institute, Chicago

Peaslee, W. D. A., Valparaiso Technical Institute, Valparaiso, Ind.*

Schram, Richard A., Chain Belt Company, Downers Grove, Ill.

Schwarz, Robert F., Purdue University Center, Michigan City, Ind.

Van Zeeland, Fred J., Milwaukee School of Engineering, Milwaukee

Advisory

Gammell, John, Allis-Chalmers Manufacturing Company, Milwaukee

REGION VII

Metz, Donald C., *Chairman,* Technical Institute, University of Dayton, Dayton, Ohio

* Deceased.

Fleckenstein, Edward L., Ohio Mechanics Institute, Cincinnati (Name changed November 1958 to Ohio College of Applied Science)

Graney, Maurice, University of Dayton, Dayton, Ohio

Miller, Kenneth, Southern Illinois University, Carbondale.

Pratt, D. F., The Cincinnati Milling Machine Company, Cincinnati

Rimboi, Nicholas R., Technical Institute, Fenn College, Cleveland

Rosener, W. C., National Cash Register Company, Dayton, Ohio

Taylor, Charles W., Fisher Body Division, General Motors Corporation, Cleveland

Region VIII

Sims, A. Ray, *Chairman,* College of Technology, University of Houston, Houston

McCallick, H. E., *Co-chairman,* College of Technology, University of Houston, Houston

Berleth, F. H., Hughes Tool Company, Houston

Bingham, R. W., College of Technology, University of Houston, Houston

Campbell, Roy E., College of Technology, University of Houston, Houston

Dossat, Roy J., College of Technology, University of Houston, Houston

FitzHugh, Parker M., College of Technology, University of Houston, Houston

Gentry, C. B., College of Technology, University of Houston, Houston

Martin, John R., College of Technology, University of Houston, Houston

McKay, George C., Jr., College of Technology, University of Houston, Houston

Whittington, H. K., College of Technology, University of Houston, Houston

Willson, William H., College of Technology, University of Houston, Houston

Advisory

Colvert, C. C., University of Texas, Austin, Tex.
Hockaday, O. S., Texas Electric Service Co., Fort Worth, Tex.
Keiller, T. M., Houston Lighting and Power Company, Houston

REGION IX

Campbell, Bonham, *Chairman,* University of California, Los Angeles
Smith, Eugene Wood, *Co-chairman,* Cogswell Polytechnical College, San Francisco
Austin, Ward H., College of Marin, Kentfield, Calif.
Brierley, Fred J., Santa Monica City College, Santa Monica, Calif.
Hartley, Herbert W., Northrop Aeronautical Institute, Inglewood, Calif. (Name changed July 1959 to Northrop Institute of Technology)
Howe, Everett D., University of California, Berkeley, Calif.
Kepley, William N., Jr., Los Angeles City Schools, Los Angeles
Mayo, William K., City College of San Francisco, San Francisco
Moses, Robert G., Pasadena City College, Pasadena, Calif.
Reid, C. T., Northrop Aeronautical Institute, Inglewood, Calif. (Name changed July 1959 to Northrop Institute of Technology)
Stockwell, Richard E., Sacramento Junior College, Sacramento, Calif.

Advisory

Holmes, J. B., General Electric Company, San Francisco

REGION X

Sanders, John C., *Chairman,* Boeing Airplane Company, Seattle

Elias, L. J., *Co-chairman,* State Board of Education, Olympia, Wash.

Avery, John H., Boeing Airplane Company, Seattle

Giles, Frederic T., Everett Junior College, Everett, Wash.

Morrison, D. Grant, Specialist, Junior and Community Colleges, U.S. Office of Education

Advisory

Chatburn, A. H., Boise Junior College, Boise, Idaho

Dever, Ralph, State Board for Vocational Education, Olympia, Wash.

Gleeson, George, Oregon State College, Corvallis, Ore.

Johnson, Walter S., Clarke College, Vancouver, Wash.

Kildow, G. O., North Idaho Junior College, Coeur d'Alene, Idaho

Kimbark, Edward W., University of Seattle, Seattle

Purvine, Winston D., Oregon Technical Institute, Klamath Falls, Ore.

Spielman, J. P., Washington State College, Pullman, Wash.

Wessman, Harold E., University of Washington, Seattle

Region XI

Johnson, L. V., *Chairman,* Georgia Institute of Technology, Atlanta

Arntson, C. A., Southern Technical Institute, Chamblee, Ga.

Edwards, Robert N., Southern Technical Institute, Chamblee, Ga.

Gignilliat, Arthur M., Armstrong College, Savannah, Ga.

Halstead, Wm. R., Gaston Technical Institute, Gastonia, N.C.

Hays, Robert, Southern Technical Institute, Chamblee, Ga.

Lyda, H. B., Associated Industries of Georgia, Atlanta, Ga.

McClure, H. L., Southern Technical Institute, Chamblee, Ga.

Thomas, Weldon L., Southern Technical Institute, Chamblee, Ga.

Advisory

Arnold, J. E., University of Tennessee, Knoxville, Tenn.

Bailey, Thurman J., State Department of Education, Talla-hassee, Fla.

Howell, Roger S., Georgia Institute of Technology, Atlanta*

Region XII

Adams, Henry P., *Chairman,* The Technical Institute, Okla-homa State University, Stillwater, Okla.

Roney, Maurice W., *Co-chairman,* The Technical Institute, Oklahoma State University, Stillwater, Okla.

Wallingford, John T., *Co-chairman,* Central Technical Insti-tute, Kansas City, Mo.

Jared, Clifford H., Northeastern Oklahoma Junior College, Tonkowa, Okla.

Robson, Fred B., Oklahoma City University, Oklahoma City, Okla.

Region XIII

Werwath, Karl O., *Chairman,* Milwaukee School of Engineer-ing, Milwaukee

Murphy, Gordon J., University of Minnesota, Minneapolis

Oleson, Kenneth S., Iowa State College, Ames, Iowa

Region XIV

Nichols, Mark, *Chairman,* Department of Public Instruction, State of Utah, Salt Lake City, Utah

Peterson, Lorenzo E., *Vice-chairman,* Weber College, Ogden, Utah

Gray, C. S., Sperry-Utah Engineering Laboratory, Salt Lake City, Utah

Harris, Dale S., University of Utah, Salt Lake City, Utah

Jonsson, Jens J., Brigham Young University, Provo, Utah

* Retired.

Advisory

Braithwaite, Royden C., College of Southern Utah, Cedar City, Utah

Christiansen, J. E., Utah State Agricultural College, Logan, Utah

Dalley, James, Weber College, Ogden, Utah

Jones, W. L., Utah State Agricultural College, Logan, Utah

Kistler, S. S., University of Utah, Salt Lake City, Utah

Miller, William P., Weber College, Ogden, Utah

Nelson, J. L., Salt Lake Trade Technical Institute, Salt Lake City, Utah

Smith, Raymond, University of Utah, Salt Lake City, Utah

Sorenson, Wilson W., Central Utah Vocational School, Provo, Utah

Wilkins, D. Frank, Radio Institute, Inc., Salt Lake City, Utah

B. *Educational Institutions*

In an effort to determine the actual extent of the zone of technical institute education, comprehensive questionnaires were mailed to the chief administrative officers of all institutions for which catalogues or other sources of information indicated offerings in post-high school technical education other than for baccalaureate degrees. Of this total of 256, a group of 166 responded. An additional 24 were identified by Regional Committees.

Of these 190 participating institutions, practically all executed a comprehensive mail questionnaire and ninety-six were personally visited by a Regional Team which augmented the questionnaire by extensive interviews with administration and faculty. Data so collected revealed 121 * of these various insti-

* As reported in Chapter 1 and elsewhere in this report, a total of 144 schools were found to be offering curriculums of technical institute nature, but only 121 furnished data adequate for Survey purposes.

tutions to be offering curricular programs competent to develop engineering technicians as defined for the purposes of
this Survey (see Chapter 2). Of these 121, thirty-six had in
1958 a total of 116 technical institute curriculums accredited
by the Engineers' Council for Professional Development. The
names of all institutes are given as of the time of visitation,
although several have since been changed. It must be emphasized that not all schools using the name "Technical Institute" are operating up to the standards of technical institute education as defined in this report.

   *1. Academy of Aeronautics, Flushing, N.Y.
   *2. Acme School of Die Design, South Bend, Ind.
    3. Aeronautical University, Chicago
    4. Alliance Technical Institute, Cambridge, Pa.
   *5. Amarillo College, Amarillo, Tex.
    6. Apprentice School of the Newport News Shipbuilding
       and Drydock Co., Newport News, Va.
    7. Arkansas Polytechnic College, Russellville, Ark.
   *8. Arlington State College, Arlington, Tex.
   *9. Armstrong College of Savannah, Savannah, Ga.
   10. Asheville-Biltmore College, Asheville, N.C.
  *11. Bakersfield College, Bakersfield, Calif.
  *12. Baltimore Junior College, Baltimore
   13. Bowman Technical School, Lancaster, Pa.
   14. Boston University, College of Industrial Technology,
       Boston
   15. Bradley University, Peoria, Ill.
  *16. Broome Technical Community College, Binghamton,
       N.Y.
   17. University of Buffalo, Division of General & Technical
       Studies, Buffalo
  *18. California State Polytechnic College, San Luis Obispo,
       Calif.
   19. Cameron State Agricultural College, Lawton, Okla.

   * Institutions visited by a Regional Team.

*20. Capitol Radio Engineering Institute, Washington

21. Carbon College, Price, Utah

22. Casper Junior College, Casper, Wyo.

*23. Central Technical Institute, Inc., Kansas City, Mo.

*24. Charlotte College, Charlotte, N.C.

25. Chicago City Junior College, Wilson Branch, Chicago

26. Chicago Technical College, Chicago

27. Chrysler Institute of Engineering, Detroit

*28. University of Cincinnati, Cincinnati

29. Clarke College, Vancouver, Wash.

*30. Cogswell Polytechnical College, San Francisco

*31. Technical Institute of University of Dayton, Dayton, Ohio

*32. Del Mar College, Corpus Christi, Tex.

33. Detroit College of Applied Science, Detroit

34. Detroit Engineering Institute, Detroit

*35. DeVry Technical Institute, Chicago

*36. Drexel Institute of Technology, Philadelphia, Pa.

*37. The William Hood Dunwoody Industrial Institute, Minneapolis

38. Eastern Arizona Junior College, Thatcher, Ariz.

*39. East Coast Aero Tech School, Lexington, Mass.

40. East Contra Costra Junior College, Concord, Calif.

41. East Los Angeles Junior College, Los Angeles

*42. Electronics Institute, Inc., Detroit

*43. Embry-Riddle Aeronautical Institute, Miami, Fla.

*44. Erie County Technical Institute, Buffalo

45. Everett Junior College, Everett, Wash.

46. Fashion Institute of Technology, New York

*47. Technical Institute of Fenn College, Cleveland

48. Flint Junior College, Flint, Mich.

*49. Florida Agricultural and Mechanical University, Tallahassee, Fla.

*50. Franklin Technical Institute, Boston

*51. Franklin University, Columbus, Ohio

* Institutions visited by a Regional Team.

52. Fresno Junior College, Fresno, Calif.
53. Fullerton Junior College, Fullerton, Calif.
*54. Gaston Technical Institute, Gastonia, N.C.
55. General Motors Institute, Flint, Mich.
56. Grand Rapids Junior College, Grand Rapids, Mich.
57. Greer Technical Institute, Chicago
*58. Henry Ford Community College, Dearborn, Mich.
59. Highland Park Community College, Highland Park, Mich.
60. Holyoke Junior College, Holyoke, Mass.
*61. University of Houston, College of Technology, Houston
62. Hudson Valley Technical Institute, Troy, N.Y.
63. Indiana Technical College, Fort Wayne, Ind.
64. Industrial Technical School, Boston
*65. Instituto Technologico de Monterrey, Monterrey, N.L., Mexico
66. Jamestown Community College, Jamestown, N.Y.
67. Joplin Junior College, Joplin, Mo.
68. Kansas State Teachers College, Pittsburg, Kansas
69. Keegan Technical Institute, Memphis, Tenn.
70. Kentucky State College, Frankfort, Ky.
71. University of Kentucky, Lexington, Ky.
*72. Kilgore College, Kilgore, Tex.
73. Lain Technical Institute, Indianapolis
*74. Lamar State College of Technology, Beaumont, Tex.
*75. The Technical Institute of Lawrence Institute of Technology, Detroit
*76. LeTourneau Technical Institute of Texas, Longview, Tex.
*77. Lewis College of Science and Technology, Lockport, Ill.
*78. Lincoln Institute of Northeastern University, Boston
79. Long Beach City College, Long Beach, Calif.
80. Los Angeles Harbor Junior College, Wilmington, Calif.
81. Los Angeles Pierce Junior College, Canoga Park, Calif.

* Institutions visited by a Regional Team.

*82. Los Angeles Trade-Technical Junior College, Los Angeles
*83. Lowell Institute School, Massachusetts Institute of Technology, Cambridge, Mass.
 84. Lowell Technological Institute, Lowell, Mass.
 84a. Maine Vocational-Technical Institute, Portland, Maine
*85. Manitoba Technical Institute, Winnipeg
*86. Mechanics Institute, New York
 87. Mesa College, Grand Junction, Colo.
 88. Midwestern College, Fort Wayne, Ind.
*89. Milwaukee School of Engineering, Milwaukee
*90. University of Minnesota, Minneapolis
 91. Mohawk Valley Technical Institute, Utica, N.Y.
 92. Monmouth Junior College, Long Branch, N.J.
*93. Montgomery Junior College, Takoma Park, Md.
 94. Mt. San Antonio Junior College, Pomona, Calif.
 95. National Schools, Los Angeles
*96. Newark College of Engineering, Special Courses Division, Newark, N.J.
*97. New Hampshire Technical Institute, Manchester, N.H.
 98. New Haven College, New Haven, Conn.
 99. Newton Junior College, Newtonville, Mass.
 100. The College of the City of New York, New York
*101. New York City Community College, Brooklyn, N.Y.
 102. State University of New York Agricultural and Technical Institute, Alfred, N.Y.
 103. State University of New York Agricultural and Technical Institute, Canton, N.Y.
 104. State University of New York Agricultural and Technical Institute, Delhi, N.Y.
 105. State University of New York Agricultural and Technical Institute, Farmingdale, N.Y.
 106. State University of New York Agricultural and Technical Institute, Morrisville, N.Y.

 * Institutions visited by a Regional Team.

107. New York University, New York
108. North Dakota State School of Science, Wahpeton, N.D.
109. Northeastern Agricultural and Mechanical College, Miami, Okla.
*110. Northrop Aeronautical Institute, Inglewood, Calif. (Name changed July 1959 to Northrop Institute of Technology)
111. Northwest Radio and Television School, Portland, Ore.
112. Northwestern Michigan College, Traverse City, Mich.
113. Oakland Junior College, Oakland, Calif.
*114. Odessa Junior College, Odessa, Tex.
*115. Ohio Mechanics Institute, Cincinnati. (Name changed November 1958 to Ohio College of Applied Science)
*116. The Ohio State University, Columbus, Ohio
*117. Ohio University, Athens, Ohio
*118. Oklahoma City University, Oklahoma City
*119. Oklahoma State University, The Technical Institute, Stillwater, Okla.
120. Olympic Junior College, Bremerton, Wash.
121. University of Omaha, Omaha
122. Orange Coast College, Costa Mesa, Calif.
*123. Orange County Community College, Middletown, N.Y.
124. Oregon Polytechnic Institute, Portland, Ore.
*125. Oregon Technical Institute, Klamath Falls, Ore.
126. Paris Junior College, Paris, Tex.
127. Pasadena City College, Pasadena, Calif.
128. Pearl River Junior College, Poplarville, Miss.
129. The Pennsylvania State University, General Extension Services, University Park, Pa.
*130. The Pennsylvania State University, McKeesport Center, McKeesport, Pa.
*131. Penn Technical Institute, Pittsburgh, Pa.
132. Philadelphia Wireless Technical Institute, Philadelphia

* Institutions visited by a Regional Team.

133. Pittsburgh Institute of Aeronautics, Pittsburgh, Pa.

134. Port Huron Junior College, Port Huron, Mich.

*135. Pratt Institute, Brooklyn, N.Y.

136. Pueblo Junior College, Pueblo, Colo.

137. Purdue University, Division of Technical Extension, Lafayette, Ind.

138. Purdue University Barker Center, Michigan City, Ind.

139. Purdue University Calumet Center, Hammond, Ind.

*140. RCA Institutes, Inc., New York

141. Radio Electronic Television Schools, Detroit

*142. Rochester Institute of Technology, Rochester, N.Y.

*143. Rutgers University, University Extension Division, New Brunswick, N.J.

*144. Ryerson Institute of Technology, Toronto

*145. Sacramento Junior College, Sacramento, Calif.

146. San Angelo College, San Angelo, Tex.

*147. San Antonio College, San Antonio, Tex.

*148. San Bernardino Valley College, San Bernardino, Calif.

*149. San Diego Junior College and Vocational School, San Diego, Calif.

*150. City College of San Francisco, San Francisco

151. San Jose Junior College, San Jose, Calif.

152. College of San Mateo, San Mateo, Calif.

*153. Santa Monica City College, Santa Monica, Calif.

*154. Savannah State College, Savannah, Ga.

*155. Sinclair College, Dayton, Ohio

156. Skagit Valley Junior College, Mount Vernon, Wash.

157. South Macomb Community College, Van Dyke, Mich.

*158. Vocational Technical Institute, Southern Illinois University, Carbondale, Ill.

*159. Southern Technical Institute, Chamblee, Ga.

*160. Southern University and A. & M. College, Baton Rouge, La.

161. Sparton School of Aeronautics, Tulsa, Okla.

* Institutions visited by a Regional Team.

*162. Speed Scientific School, University of Louisville, Louisville, Ky.
*163. Spring Garden Institute, Philadelphia
*164. State Technical Institute, Hartford, Conn.
 165. Staten Island Community College, Staten Island, N.Y.
*166. Stevens Institute of Technology, Hoboken, N.J.
 167. Stockton College, Stockton, Calif.
 168. Taft College, Taft, Calif.
*169. Temple University, Technical Institute, Philadelphia
 170. Texas Southern University, Houston
*171. University of Toledo, Toledo, Ohio
*172. Trenton Junior College, Trenton, N.J.
*173. Tulane University of Louisiana, New Orleans
 174. Tyler Junior College, Tyler, Tex.
*175. Valparaiso Technical Institute, Valparaiso, Ind.
 176. University of Virginia, Charlottesville, Va.
*177. Ward School of Electronics, University of Hartford, Hartford, Conn.
 178. Washington Radio & Television Institute, Seattle
*179. Wentworth Institute, Boston
*180. Westchester Community College, White Plains, N.Y.
 181. Western Michigan College of Education, Kalamazoo, Mich.
*182. Westinghouse Technical Night School, East Pittsburgh, Pa.
 183. West Virginia Institute of Technology, Montgomery, W.Va.
 184. College of William & Mary, Norfolk, Va.
 185. Roger Williams Junior College, Providence
*186. Williamsport Technical Institute, Williamsport, Pa.
*187. Worcester Junior College, Worcester, Mass.
 188. Wyomissing Polytechnic Institute, Wyomissing, Pa.
*189. Youngstown University, Youngstown, Ohio
        Total: 190

* Institutions visited by a Regional Team.

C. Industrial Concerns and Other Employers
Visited by a Regional Team

1. AC Spark Plug Div., General Motors Corp., Milwaukee
2. Allis-Chalmers Mfg. Co., Milwaukee
3. American Can Company, San Francisco
4. American Cyanamid Co., Calco Chemical Div., Bound Brook, N.J.
4a. American Optical Company, Southbridge, Mass.
5. American Telephone & Telegraph Co., Long Lines Dept., White Plains, N.Y.
6. Anaconda Wire & Cable Co., Hastings-on-Hudson, N.Y.
7. Associated General Contractors, Tulsa, Okla.
8. Atlantic Steel Co., Atlanta, Tex.
9. AVCO, Lycoming Div., Williamsport, Pa.
10. The Babcock & Wilcox Company, Scranton, Pa.
11. The Bailey Co., Inc., Amesbury, Mass.
12. Bell Telephone Laboratories, Inc., New York
13. Bendix Aviation Corporation, Kansas City, Mo.
14. Bendix Products Div., South Bend, Ind.
15. The Black & Decker Mfg. Co., Towson, Md.
16. Black, Sivalls & Byrson, Inc., Oil & Gas Equipment Div., Oklahoma City, Okla.
17. Boeing Airplane Company, Seattle
18. Boeing Airplane Company, Wichita, Kans.
19. Brown & Sharpe Mfg. Co., Providence
20. Bryant Electric Repair Co., Inc., Gastonia, N.C.
21. Burroughs Corp., Detroit
22. California Div. of Highways, District 4, San Francisco
23. California Div. of Highways, Headquarters, Sacramento, Calif.
24. California Electric Power Co., Riverside, Calif.
25. Canada Wire & Cable Co., Ltd., Toronto
26. Canadian General Electric Co., Ltd., Electronics Div., Toronto
27. Canadian Industries Ltd., Paint & Varnish Div., Toronto

28. Cardinal Chemical Company, Odessa, Tex.
29. Carter Oil Company, Tulsa, Okla.
30. Celorex, S.A., Monterrey, N.L., Mexico
31. Charles Pfizer & Co., Brooklyn, N.Y.
32. Chrysler Corp., Automotive Engineering Div., Detroit
33. Chrysler Corp., Missile Operations, Detroit
34. The Cincinnati Milling Machine Co., Cincinnati
35. Consolidated Edison of New York, New York
36. Consolidated Electrodynamics Corporation, Pasadena, Calif.
37. Convair, Inc., Fort Worth, Tex.
38. Cook Electric Co., Chicago
39. Corn Products Refining Co., Corpus Christi, Tex.
40. Curtiss-Wright Corp., Metal Processing Div., Buffalo
41. Dalmo, Victor, Inc., Belmont, Calif.
42. Daystrom Instrument Company, Eynon, Pa.
43. Detroit Edison Company, Detroit
44. Douglas Aircraft Co., Inc., Charlotte, N.C.
45. Duke Power Company, Charlotte, N.C.
46. E. I. DuPont de Nemours & Co., Inc., Sabine River Works, Orange, Tex.
47. Duquesne Light Company, Pittsburgh, Pa.
48. Eastman Kodak Co., Rochester, N.Y.
49. Engineering Sound Systems, Ltd., Toronto
50. Esso Standard Oil Co., Baton Rouge, La.
51. Ethyl Corp., Baton Rouge, La.
52. Fabricas Monterrey, S.A., Monterrey, N.L., Mexico
53. The Fellows Gear Shaper Company, Springfield, Vt.
54. Ford Motor Company, Detroit
55. The Foxboro Company, Foxboro, Mass.
56. Friedrich Refrigerators, Inc., San Antonio, Tex.
57. Fulton Bag & Cotton Mills, Atlanta
58. General Dynamics Co., Electric Boat Div., Groton, Conn.
59. General Electric Company, Cincinnati
60. General Electric Company, Home Heating & Cooling Plant, Tyler, Tex.

61. General Motors Corp., Fisher Body Div., Detroit
62. General Precision Laboratory, Inc., Pleasantville, N.Y.
63. The Glenn L. Martin Co., Baltimore
64. Great Northern Paper Co., Millinocket, Maine
65. Gulf Research & Development Co., Pittsburgh
66. Hanford Foundry Co., San Bernardino, Calif.
67. Heat & Control Co., San Francisco
68. Houston Lighting & Power Co., Houston
69. Hughes Aircraft Co., Aircraft Field Services & Support Div., Culver City, Calif.
70. Hughes Aircraft Co., Products Group, Culver City, Calif.
71. Hughes Aircraft Co., El Segundo Div., Segundo, Calif.
72. Hughes Research & Development Laboratories, Culver City, Calif.
73. Hughes Tool Co., Houston
74. I-T-E Circuit Breaker Co., Philadelphia
75. Industrial Research Services, Toronto
76. International Business Machines Corp., Los Angeles
77. International Business Machines Corp., New York
78. International Business Machines Corp., Products Development Lab., Endicott, N.Y.
79. International Business Machines Corp., Sales Office, Cincinnati
80. International Derrick & Equipment Co., Beaumont, Tex.
81. Johns-Manville Research Center, Manville, N.J.
82. Johnson & Johnson, New Brunswick, N.J.
83. Jones Tool & Die Co., Miami, Fla.
84. Lincoln Electric of Canada, Ltd., Toronto
85. Link Aviation, Inc., Binghamton, N.Y.
85a. Arthur D. Little Company, Inc., Cambridge, Mass.
86. McGill Mfg. Co., Inc., Valparaiso, Ind.
87. Midwest Research Institute, Kansas City, Mo.
88. Minneapolis-Honeywell Regulator Co., Minneapolis
89. Monsanto Chemical Co., Springfield, Mass.
90. Motorola, Inc., Chicago, Ill.
91. National Cash Register Co., Dayton, Ohio

92. Naval Air Material Center, Philadelphia
93. New Orleans Public Service, Inc., New Orleans
94. New York Naval Shipyard, Brooklyn, N.Y.
95. Norton Company, Worcester, Mass.
96. North American Aviation, Inc., Columbus, Ohio
97. North American Aviation, Inc., Los Angeles
98. Oklahoma Gas & Electric Co., Oklahoma City, Okla.
99. Pacific Gas & Electric Co., Main Office, San Francisco
100. Pan American World Airways, Miami, Fla.
101. Parke, Davis & Co., Detroit
102. Philco Corporation, Philadelphia
103. Phillips Petroleum Co., Bartlesville, Okla.
104. Pittsburgh Plate Glass Co., Pittsburgh
105. Procter & Gamble Co., Ivorydale Plant, Cincinnati
106. Puget Sound Naval Shipyard, Bremerton, Wash.
107. RCA Laboratories Div., Princeton, N.J.
108. RCA, West Coast Electronics Dept., West Los Angeles, Calif.
109. Raytheon Mfg. Co., Waltham, Mass.
110. Republic Aviation Corp., Farmingdale, L.I., N.Y.
111. Reynolds Metals Company, Corpus Christi, Tex.
112. Savannah Sugar Refining Corp., Savannah, Ga.
113. Shell Oil Co., Tulsa, Okla.
114. Sivalls Tanks, Inc., Odessa, Tex.
115. SKF Industries, Inc., Atlas Ball Div., Philadelphia
116. Southern Pacific Co., Civil Engineering Dept., San Francisco
117. Southwest Research Institute, San Antonio, Tex.
118. Sprague Electric Co., North Adams, Mass.
119. Steel Company of Canada, Ltd., Hamilton, Canada
120. Sylvania Electric Products, Inc., Photolamp Div., Montoursville, Pa.
121. Sylvania Electric Products, Inc., Tube Div., Williamsport, Pa.
122. Texas Electric Service Co., Fort Worth, Tex.
123. Transonic, Inc., Bakersfield, Calif.

124. Trico Products Mfg. Co., Buffalo
125. Tyler Pipe & Foundry, Tyler, Tex.
126. Union Bag & Paper Corp., Savannah, Ga.
127. Union Carbide & Carbon Corporation, New York
128. Union Oil Co., Bakersfield, Calif.
129. United Aircraft Corp., Pratt & Whitney Div., East Hartford, Conn.
130. United-Carr Fastener Corp., Cambridge, Mass.
131. U.S. Naval Air Missile Test Center, Point Mugu, Calif.
132. United States Steel Corporation, Pittsburgh, Pa.
133. Vendo Corporation, Kansas City, Mo.
134. Ward Leonard Electric Co., Mt. Vernon, N.Y.
135. Westinghouse Electric Corporation, East Pittsburgh, Pa.
135a. Winchester Arms Division, Olin Mathieson Chemical Corp., New Haven, Conn.
136. Wright Aeronautical Div., Curtiss-Wright Corp., Woodridge, N.J.
137. Wright-Patterson Air Force Base, Dayton, Ohio
138. Wyandotte Chemicals Corp., Wyandotte, Mich.
139. Wyman-Gordon Co., Grafton Plant, Worcester, Mass.
140. Youngstown Sheet & Tube Co., Youngstown, Ohio
    Total: 143

Appendix 2. Typical occupational opportunities as related to curricular technology areas

Representative Curricular Areas	*Typical Occupational Titles*
Aeronautical technologies Research Design Development Production Maintenance	Aircraft Flight Technician Aircraft Instrument Technician Aircraft Maintenance Supervisor Aircraft Parts Inspector Airframe Structure Test Technician Draftsman Engineering Liaison Technician Final Assembly Inspector Flight Engineer Flight Line Inspector Power Plant Test Technician Production Controller Production Planner Quality Control Technician Stress Analyst Systems Technician Technical Field Representative Technical Writer Test Data Analyst Test Laboratory Technician Wind Tunnel Technician
Air conditioning, heating, and refrigeration technologies Research Design Development Manufacturing	Applications Specialist Contractor or Dealer Controls Specialist Development Technician Draftsman Estimator and Layout Technician Heat Pump Specialist

Representative Curricular Areas	*Typical Occupational Titles*
Installation Service	Heating Plant Superintendent Industrial and Commercial Equipment Designer Installation Supervisor Laboratory Test Technician Manufacturer's Representative Quality Control Technician Research Assistant Residential Equipment Designer Sales Representative System Designer Test and Service Specialist
Building construction technologies Research Design Construction Maintenance Sales	Architectural Draftsman Building Contractor Building Inspector Construction Foreman Construction Assistant Engineering Aide Estimator Expediter Equipment Sales Representative Manufacturer's Representative Materials Tester Materials Sales Representative Research Assistant Structural Design Draftsman Structural Inspector
Chemical technologies Research Development Production Sales	Analyst Assistant Chemist Chemical Operator (production) Chemical Technician Junior Chemist Laboratory Assistant Laboratory Supervisor Laboratory Technician Manufacturer's Sales Representative

Representative Curricular Areas	Typical Occupational Titles
	Paper Technician
	Pilot Plant Operator (research and development)
	Plastics Technician
	Production Control Technician
	Production Supervisor
	Quality Control Technician
	Research Assistant
	Sampler
	Technical Illustrator
	Technical Writer
Civil technologies	Assistant to Consulting Engineer
Research	Computer
Design	Construction Supervisor
Development	Design Draftsman
Construction	Engineering Assistant
Maintenance	Engineering Draftsman
	Estimator
	Highway Engineering Technician
	Instrument Man
	Laboratory Technician (research and development)
	Map Draftsman
	Materials Tester
	Materials Inspector
	Photogrammetrist
	Research Analyst
	Structural Design Draftsman
	Structural Inspector
	Survey Party Chief
	Specifications Writer
	Technical Writer
Drafting technologies	Application Specialist
Research	Architectural Draftsman
Design	Design Draftsman
Development	Detailer

Representative Curricular Areas	*Typical Occupational Titles*
Production	Customer Service Specialist
Construction	Electrical Draftsman
	Electronic Draftsman
	Junior Designer
	Layout Draftsman
	Manufacturer's Sales Representative
	Map Draftsman
	Mechanical Draftsman
	Model Maker
	Plant Layout Designer
	Product Designer
	Production Layout Draftsman
	Research Analyst
	Tool and Die Designer
Electrical technologies	Applications Specialist
Research	Controls Specialist
Design	Electrical Contractor
Development	Electrical Draftsman
Production	Electrical Motor Analyst
Maintenance	Equipment Designer
Sales	Field Service Specialist
	Laboratory Technician
	Line Supervisor
	Manufacturer's Sales Representative
	Meter and Instrument Technician
	Power Station Operator
	Product Designer
	Production Control Technician
	Production Process Technician
	Project Supervisor
	Quality Control Technician
	Rectifier Technician
	Relay Specialist
	Research Assistant
	Technical Illustrator
	Technical Writer

Representative Curricular Areas	*Typical Occupational Titles*

Electronic technologies
  Research
  Design
  Development
  Production
  Maintenance
  Sales
	Aircraft Electronic Technician
	Chief, Broadcast Transmitter Engineer
	Communication Supervisor
	Communication Technician
	Computer Technician
	Customer Service Technician
	Design Draftsman
	Electronic Control Technician
	Electronic Draftsman
	Equipment Designer
	Guided Missile Technician
	Industrial Control Specialist
	Industrial Electronic Technician
	Laboratory Technician
	Manufacturer's Sales Representative
	Production Process Technician
	Production Control Technician
	Quality Control Technician
	Radar Technician
	Research Analyst
	Technical Writer

Industrial technologies
  Research
  Design
  Development
  Production
  Maintenance
	Application Specialist
	Assistant Production Supervisor
	Cost Control Technician
	Estimator
	Industrial Technician
	Installation Specialist
	Laboratory Technician
	Manufacturing Supervisor
	Manufacturing Technician
	Materials Control Technician
	Methods Analyst
	Motion and Time Study Analyst
	Plant Layout Technician
	Plant Results Analyst

Representative Curricular Areas	*Typical Occupational Titles*
	Product Engineering Technician
	Production Control Technician
	Production Planning Technician
	Production Process Technician
	Quality Control Technician
	Research Assistant
Mechanical technologies	Applications Specialist
Research	Assistant Metallurgist
Design	Chief Inspector
Development	Control Technician
Production	Design Draftsman
Maintenance	Field Service Technical Representative
Sales	
	Materials Control Technician
	Machine Design Technician
	Mechanical Draftsman
	Methods Analyst
	Plant Layout Technician
	Product Designer
	Production Control Technician
	Production Expediter
	Production Process Technician
	Quality Control Technician
	Research Assistant
	Sales Representative
	Stress Analyst
	Technical Writer
	Tool and Die Designer
Power technologies	Automotive Diesel Technician
Research	Boiler and Machinery Inspector
Design	Compressor Station Technician
Development	Customer Service Technician
Production	Design Draftsman
Maintenance	Development Technician

Representative Curricular Areas	Typical Occupational Titles
Sales	Diesel Electric Technician
	Diesel Marine Technician
	Field Service Technical Representative
	Instrument Technician
	Laboratory Assistant
	Manufacturer's Sales Representative
	Mechanical Draftsman
	Production Designer
	Production Control Technician
	Production Process Technician
	Quality Control Technician
	Research Assistant
	Stress Analyst
	Test Laboratory Technician
	Test Procedure Technician

Appendix 3. Typical technical institute curriculums and related course descriptions

(All accredited by Engineers' Council for Professional Development, school year, 1956–1957)

Curriculum in Industrial Electronics

Gives instruction for the purpose of meeting standards of quality in the field of electronics as applied to the technical rather than the engineering field. Leads to diploma as Engineering Aide.

First Year

FIRST SEMESTER—ELECTRONIC FUNDAMENTALS

		Lecture hours	Laboratory hours	Credits
101	Physics I	30	10	1
102	Mathematics I	45	35	2
103	D-c Fundamentals and Magnetism	75	45	3
104	A-c Fundamentals	75	45	3
106	Measurements I	20	20	1
107	Circuit Drawing and Layout	10	30	1
108	Technical Writing I	30	10	1
110	Vacuum Tube Principles	75	45	3
	Total	360	240	15

SECOND SEMESTER—CIRCUIT ANALYSIS AND THEORY

		Lecture hours	Laboratory hours	Credits
202	Applied Mathematics I	45	35	2
206	Measurements II	50	30	2
208	Technical Writing II	30	10	1
210	Vacuum Tube Circuits I	100	60	4
220	Modulation Principles	45	35	2
230	Field Theory I	45	35	2
240	Complex Waveform Analysis	45	35	2
	Total	360	240	15

205

Second Year

FIRST SEMESTER—INDUSTRIAL ELECTRONICS

		Lec- ture hours	Labo- ratory hours	Credits
501	Physics II	20	20	1
502	Applied Mathematics IV	50	30	2
506	Industrial Measurements	45	35	2
508	Technical Report Writing III	20	20	1
510	Gas-tubes and Circuits	80	40	3
511	Automatic Control	50	30	2
513	Electronic Relays	45	35	2
551	Transducers and Special Devices	50	30	2
	Total	360	240	15

SECOND SEMESTER—INDUSTRIAL INSTRUMENTATION

601	Physics III	50	30	2
602	Applied Mathematics V	30	10	1
607	Advanced Drawing I	10	30	1
608	Technical Report Writing IV	20	20	1
616	Process Instruments for Measurements	75	45	3
626	Process Instruments for Control	100	60	4
636	Process Instruments for Transmission	75	45	3
	Total	360	240	15

Course descriptions

Physics I (101). This course is designed to give the students an understanding of the principles and laws of physics encountered in a technical field. It involves the laws of matter and energy, forces and their components, vector analysis, moments, torque, motion, balance of nature, and standards of measurements.

Mathematics I (102). Review of the fundamentals of algebra and presentation of trigonometric functions as applied to electronics. It covers the following topics: signed numbers, rules of transposition, powers of ten; use of the slide rule to multiply, divide, raise to a power, extract a root, find logarithms, and solve proportions; powers, exponents, logarithms, decibels, rectangular and polar coordinates, imaginary numbers, trigonometric functions, relationships, plotting, and interpreting graphs.

D-c Fundamentals and Magnetism (103). A study of the laws and actions of direct current in an electric circuit. Some of the topics covered are: resistance, voltage, current, static electricity, Ohm's law, d-c power, development and storage of electricity, capacitance, time constants, magnetism, electromagnetism, mutual inductance, and self-inductance.

A-c Fundamentals (104). Development of the sine wave, peak, average and effective values, resistive a-c circuits, reactive a-c circuits, resistive and reactive a-c circuits, a-c power, power factor, transformers, series and parallel resonance, motors and generators.

Measurements I (106). Design and operation of meters and meter movements; use of meters to measure current, voltage, and resistance; theory, operation, and use of the oscilloscope, multimeters, multipliers, and shunts; special meters including thermocouples, RF meters, wattmeters, and galvanometers.

Circuit Drawing and Layout (107). Electronic symbols, layout principles for schematics, interpreting schematics, pictorial diagrams, principles of chassis layout; principles of drafting, free hand drawing.

Technical Writing I (108). Securing and compiling information, making outlines, intelligent notetaking, making the laboratory report, writing a business letter, compiling the résumé.

Vacuum Tube Principles (110). Election emission, diode tube parameters, rectification, diode tube circuits, multi-elements and multi-unit tubes as well as their dynamic and static parameters, interpretation of V.T. data, gas-filled tubes, classes of V.T. operation, voltage and power amplification, audio amplifiers, tuned amplifiers, frequency response and bandwidth, oscillators, semiconductors.

Applied Mathematics I (202). Mathematical formulae and their application to electronics, vectors relationships, use of mathematics in predicting operation of vacuum tube circuits, use of mathematics in determining the performance of vacuum tube circuits, use of mathematical relationships in trouble shooting, complex algebraic notation.

Measurements II (206). Measuring impedance, Q, bandwidth of tuned circuits; use of Wheatstone Bridge, impedance bridge, Q meter; use of oscilloscope to measure amplitude, frequency and phase; power, frequency, and modulation measurements in electronic circuits.

Technical Writing II (208). How to state objectives of experiments, preparation and use of schematics and block diagrams, summarizing the results of laboratory experiments.

Vacuum Tube Circuits I (210). Uses of vacuum tubes, power and signal rectifiers, electronic voltage regulators, tuned and untuned amplifiers, oscillators; voltage, current, and power requirements of vacuum tube circuits; coupling networks, feedback principles in amplifiers, reactance tube circuits, determining correct components for vacuum tube circuits, transistor circuits.

Modulation Principles (220). Types and methods of modulation including amplitude, frequency, phase and pulse modulation; frequency spectrum of modulated waves.

Field Theory I (230). Electrostatic and electromagnetic field theory; induction, radiation, coupling, and shielding.

Complex Waveform Analysis (240). Sinusoidal and nonsinusoidal response of *RL, RC,* and *RCL* circuits; transient response in *RL, RC,* and *RCL* circuits; visual waveform analysis, using the oscilloscope.

Physics II (501). Energy principles, transfer of energy, energy dissipation and storage, heat and temperature; simple optics of lenses and reflectors, nature of light, frequency, intensity, losses; response of human eye, color and light filters.

Applied Mathematics IV (502). The use of simultaneous equations, use of graphs to solve simultaneous equations, exponentials and natural logarithms, summation and rate of change (integration and differentiation).

Industrial Measurements (506). Methods of measurement of electrical quantities; laboratory measurements of frequency, phase, voltage, current, resistance, reactance, impedance, power; use of potentiometer, Kelvin Bridge, megohmmeter, Megger, Strobotac, phase-sequence detector, clip-on ammeter, frequency meter, and extreme sensitivity d-c and a-c instrument amplifiers; instrument calibration and trouble shooting; counters, scalers, and simple computers.

Technical Writing III (508). The engineering report; format, analyzing experimental results, construction of graphs for reports, error and correction charts.

Gas-tubes and Circuits (510). Characteristics of gas-tubes, ratings and nomenclature of gas-tubes; phanotrons, thyratrons, and ignitrons; grid control of gas-tube rectifiers, the inverse parallel connection of grid-controlled rectifiers; multiphase rectifiers, voltage regulators, gas-tube light sources, glow-tube oscillators, inverters; the effects of reactive loads on gas-tube rectifiers.

Automatic Control (511). Principles of control, feedback, selsyns, servomechanisms, motor speed and torque control; resistance welding controls, weld timer, sequence timers, synchronous timers, heat control; side and cutoff register controls, heating and light dimming controls, voltage regulators; electronic heating.

Electronic Relays (513). Characteristic of electromechanical relays, principles of electronic relays, contact relays, self-latching relays; time constants and time delay, time delay relays; photo tubes and light sensitive devices, the photoelectric relay, heat relays; trouble shooting relay circuits; fail-safe principles.

Transducers and Special Devices (551). Transducer principles, temperature-sensitive resistances, thyrite-materials thermocouples, bolometers and thermistors, strain gages, radiation detectors, vacuum gages, Geiger-Mueller tubes, saturable reactors, magnetic amplifiers, resistance and reactance amplifiers, electrometers, peaking transformers, differentiating and integrating circuits, wave shaping, filters, and coupling networks.

Physics III (601). The study of those phases of the general field of physics related to motion of linkages, mechanical equilibrium, pressure and density of gases and liquids, hydraulics, fluid flow, temperatures, heat as it affects matter, thermoelectricity, and humidity.

Applied Mathematics V (602). The application of algebra to the problems of conversion of pressure units, conversion of temperature scales, handling of the gas laws, interpolation in thermocouple and humidity tables, calculation of flow-equation constants, and orifice sizes in flow installations.

Advanced Drawing I (607). The standard practices and techniques used for making mechanical and freehand drawings, sketches, and schematics in cross-section, oblique projection, phantom illustration, and combined mechanical and electrical representation.

Technical Report Writing IV (608). The art and technique of presenting essential technical information in written form, as applied to the making of standard procedures, descriptive outlines, statements of rules and regulations, summarizations of projects, and analyses of functional operations of mechanisms or groupings of equipment.

Process Instruments for Measurements (616). The study of different types and makes of instruments used for measuring, indicating, and recording pressure, temperature, liquid level, differential pressure, flow, relative humidity, force, acidity-alkalinity, and chemical composition. The course includes both theory and practice in methods of operation, methods of calibration, and methods of servicing; covers both mechanical and pneumatic as well as electrical and electronic variations.

Process Instruments for Control I (626). The study of different types and makes of instruments used for controlling the process variables listed. The course includes theory and practice on methods of operation, methods of adjustment and alignment, and methods of application of control to typical

Analysis of Curriculum in Industrial Electronics

Curriculum	Total contact hours				
	Major technical specialty	Allied technical specialty	Mathematics	Lab	"General" subjects (English and communications)
Industrial Electronics......	655	515	170	990	100
1. Physics..............	...	100	...	80	
2. Mathematics.........	...	...	170	110	
3. Basic Elec.—A-c & D-c	150	...	...	90	
4. Electrical Instruments & Measurements......	115	...	...	95	
5. Circuit Drawing & Layout..............	...	10	...	30	
6. Mechanical Drawing ..	...	10	...	30	
7. Technical Report Writing..............	...	...	...	60	100
8. Vacuum-tube Principles Circuits..........	255	...	...	145	
9. Modulation Principles .	45	...	...	35	
10. Field Theory.........	45	...	...	35	
11. Complex Waveform Analysis..............	45	...	...	35	
12. Automatic Controls....	...	50	...	30	
13. Electronic Relays......	...	45	...	35	
14. Transducers and Special Devices..........	...	50	...	30	
15. Process Instruments....	...	250	...	150	

Total contact hours: Class 1440, Lab 990, Shop 0—Total 2430

process problems; also covers mechanical, pneumatic, electrical, and electronic variations and essential auxiliary equipment.

Process Instruments for Transmission I (636). The study of those special variations of instruments used in transmitting measurements and control from one place to another in pneumatic transmission, telemetering, graphic panel instrumentation, and centralized control installations. The course includes theory and practice of over-all operations, individual instrument operations, individual instrument adjustment and servicing, and over-all trouble-shooting; and covers mechanical, pneumatic, electrical and electronic variations and auxiliary equipment.

Curriculum in Structural Design Technology

A curriculum of two school years requiring a minimum of 95 credits for a diploma in Structural Design Technology is designed to qualify the graduate for work in the varied jobs which require the application of engineering principles to design or production in the structural phases of modern industry. Practical elements of engineering drawing and mathematics plus basic training in shop procedures, physics, strength of materials, and allied subjects make this a broad course of study. All subjects in the curriculum have been selected because of their direct application to industry. Leads to Associate in Applied Science degree.

First Year
FALL TERM

	Credit	Contact hours per week
Drawing (121)	4	8
Mathematics (141)	4	4
Surveying (121)	5	11
Elective	3	3
	16	26

WINTER TERM

	Credit	Contact hours per week
Drawing (122)	4	8
Mathematics (142)	4	4
Physics (112)	4	4
Strength of Materials (112)	4	4
	16	20

SPRING TERM

	Credit	Contact hours per week
Physics (112)	4	4
Strength of Materials (113)	4	4
Surveying (123)	5	11
Elective	3	3
	16	22

Second Year

FALL TERM

	Credit	Contact hours per week
Graphic Statics (224)	4	8
Mathematics (224)	5	9
Industrial Materials and Processes	3	5
Elective	3	3
	15	25

WINTER TERM

	Credit	Contact hours per week
Drawing (225)	2	5
Timber Structures (225)	4	8
Cabinet Design (225)	3	5
Reproduction Processes (225)	3	5
Elective	3	3
	15	26

SPRING TERM

	Credit	Contact hours per week
Applied Electricity (226)	5	7
Concrete Design (226)	3	6
Structural Design Projects (226)	6	12
Elective	3	3
	17	28

Recommended electives: Methods of study, first term; English composition, third term; Technical Report Writing, fifth term.

Course descriptions

Applied Electricity (226). Lecture and demonstrations covering direct current and alternating current generation, applications of d-c, inductance, and capacitance. Principles of a-c and d-c motors. General lab work mainly on an observation basis.

Cabinet Design (225). A combination of cabinet designing and craft procedure study. Drawings are made in the cabinet shop of cabinets in the process of construction and of proposed construction. Cutting bills are made and general lumber information is studied.

Concrete Design (226). The practical application of standard design practice. Problems are given in simple beams, continuous beams, "T" girders, slabs, footings, columns, retaining walls, and stairs.

Drawing (121). Provides extensive drill in basic drawing. The following areas are studied; orthographic, auxiliaries, sections, pictorial, dimensioning, fasteners, print reading, and detail drawings.

Drawing (122). Combines two phases of drawing and an element of structural blueprint reading. First, the drawing includes precision technique, and second, practical elements of descriptive geometry. The print reading includes introduction to typical structural arrangements and nomenclature as they apply to construction. Given through the medium of extensive reading from structural plans ranging from dwellings to industrial structures.

Drawing (225). The theory and practice of perspective drawing along with sketching techniques for production illustration.

Graphic Statics (224). Analysis of trussed structures by both graphical and mathematical methods.

Industrial Materials and Processes (224). Metal casting; sand, permanent mold, die, shell, investment. Plastics; thermosets, thermoplastics, laminates, coatings, adhesives. Machine processes; lathe, milling machine, shaper, drill saws. Welding processes; gas, arc, percussion, press, inert gas, brazing, soldering. Heat treating.

Mathematics (141). A short review of simple algebra and of arithmetic process followed by introduction to the use of the slide rule in its ordinary applications. The use of logarithms in their application to engineering problems, plus basic graph work, completes the course.

Mathematics (142). An introduction to simple plane trigonometry designed to give the student proficiency in applying trigonometric functions to engineering problems. It is limited to that part of trigonometry having direct bearing on the practical side of engineering practice. Prerequisite: Mathematics 141 or the equivalent.

Mathematics (224). Machine shop mathematics. Precision measuring, standard formula application, layouts involving trigonometry, gear and pulley problems.

Physics (112). Mechanics: Measurement, properties and structure of matter (solids, liquids, and gases), work, power, energy, and simple machines. Prerequisite: Mathematics 111 or the equivalent, previously or concurrently.

Physics (113). Heat, light, sound, and introduction to atomic physics. Prerequisite: Mathematics 111 or the equivalent, previously or concurrently.

Reproduction Processes (225). Study and practice in the various methods of reproducing engineering drawings and other base copy. Special emphasis is given to the planning of proper original copy to suit the particular reproduction process.

Strength of Materials (112 & 113). A basic study of forces, stress and strain, and their effects on materials.

Structural Design Projects (226). Analysis and detailing or redesigning of existing physical structures. The projects range from small cranes to elements of large structures.

Surveying (121 & 123). A comprehensive coverage of the subject of plane surveying for the purpose of learning the

Analysis of Curriculum in Structural Design Technology

Curriculum	Total contact hours					
	Major technical specialty	Allied technical specialty	Mathematics	Lab	"General" subjects	
					English and communications	Other
Structural Design Technology........	276	312	132	816	72	72
1. Drawing.........	...	...	...	252		
2. Mathematics.....	...	...	132	72		
3. Surveying........	...	96	...	168		
4. Elective.........	...	36	...	...	72	72
5. Physics..........	...	96				
6. Strength of Materials........	96					
7. Graphic Statics...	24	...	...	72		
8. Industrial Materials & Processes..	36					
9. Timber Structures	24	...	...	72		
10. Cabinet Design...	24	...	...	36		
11. Reproduction Processes........	...	36				
12. Applied Elec.....	...	48	...	36		
13. Concrete Design..	36	...	...	36		
14. Struct. Design Proj.............	36	...	...	72		

Total contact hours: Class 864, Lab 816, Shop 0—Total 1680

basic concepts and practices of all ordinary surveying procedures. This subject with its broad coverage is also designed to serve as a service course for those students in other engineering courses whose curriculums require credits in plane surveying.

Recommended electives

English Composition. Frequent written compositions with emphasis on clarity and accuracy.

Methods of Study (101). Specific methods of study as applied to various subject-matter fields; the general principles of note taking; study schedule; fixing study habits; and evaluation of the various broad fields of human learning.

Technical Report Writing (207). Application of principles to specific needs and interests of students having papers in progress. Prerequisite: English Composition 101 or the equivalent.

Curriculum in Electrical Engineering Technology

This program provides training for such technical positions in the electrical industry as electronics technician, supervisor, engineering assistant, electrical draftsman, inspector, tester, equipment installer, maintenance technician, power plant operator, and technical salesman. The Associate of Science Degree is awarded for successful completion of this curriculum.

Course descriptions

Chemistry (10A and 10B). A basic course in inorganic chemistry with practical applications. It includes a brief description of organic chemistry. The laboratory experiments and demonstrations illustrate the chemical principles. Some industrial analyses are performed in the second semester. Laboratory work and demonstrations constitute approximately half the time spent in chemistry.

Electrical Design (20A and 20B). Assigned problems in the

First Year

FIRST SEMESTER (23 Weeks)

	Semester hours credit	Class hours per week	
		Lecture	Laboratory
Chemistry 10A (Industrial Chem.)	3	3	4
Electricity 10A (D-c Circuits)	1½	3	0
Engineering Drawing 10A	3	1	7
English 10A (Writing & Speaking)	½	1	0
Mathematics 10A	3	6	0
Mechanics 10A	1½	3	0
Metal Laboratory 10A	1	0	4
Physics Laboratory 10A	2	0	7
Psychology 10A (Human Relations)	½	1	0
Cooperative Work (average of 12 weeks)			
Total, 11 weeks	16	18	22

SECOND SEMESTER (24 Weeks)

	Semester hours credit	Lecture	Laboratory
Chemistry 10B (Industrial Chem.)	3	3	4
Electricity 10B (D-c Machinery)	1½	3	0
Engineering Drawing 10B	3	1	7
English 10B (Writing & Speaking)	½	1	0
Mathematics 10B	3	6	0
Mechanics 10B	1½	3	0
Natural History 10B	½	1	0
Metal Laboratory 10B	½	0	2
Physics Laboratory 10B	2	0	7
Psychology 10B (Human Relations)	½	1	0
Technical Reading 10B	½	1	0
Cooperative Work (average of 14 weeks)			
Total, 10 weeks	16½	20	20

Second Year

FIRST SEMESTER (23 Weeks)

	Semester hours credit	Class hours per week Lecture	Class hours per week Laboratory
Electrical Design 20A	1½	0	4
Electricity 20A (A-c Circuits)	2	4	0
Electronics 20A	1½	3	0
Electronics Laboratory 20A	½	0	2
Engineering Laboratory 20A	1½	0	4
English 20A (Writing & Speaking)	½	1	0
Industrial Supervision 20A	1	2	0
Mathematics 20A	3	6	0
Mechanics 20A	1½	0	4
Metal Laboratory 20A	2	0	6
Strength of Materials 20A	2	4	0
Cooperative Work (average of 12 weeks)			
Total, 11 weeks	17	20	20

SECOND SEMESTER (20 Weeks)

Electrical Design 20B	3	0	8
Electricity 20B (A-c Machinery)	2	4	0
Electronics 20B	1½	3	0
Electronics Laboratory 20B	½	0	2
Engineering Laboratory 20B	1½	0	4
English 20B (Writing & Speaking)	½	1	0
Industrial Supervision 20B	1	2	0
Mathematics 20B	3	6	0
Metal Laboratory 20B	2	0	6
Strength of Materials 20B	2	4	0
Cooperative Work (average of 10 weeks)			
Total, 10 weeks	17	20	20

design of motors, motor controls or transformers; specifications, parts, lists, and assembly methods. Economical design is carefully considered in each problem.

Electricity (10A and 10B). The fundamentals of direct-current circuits and machines, including demonstrations and problems; units and definitions, magnetism and magnetic current, resistance and Ohm's Law, d-c circuit problems, elements of d-c machines, principles of inductance and capacitance.

Electricity (20A). (A-c Circuits) A study of a-c circuits; single-phase, polyphase; metering; solutions by $R + jx$, and G.B.Y. methods, transmission, distribution of a-c power systems; supervised problems.

Electricity (20B). (A-c Machinery) A study of a-c generators and motors; motor control and motor application; transformers, synchronous machinery; analysis of characteristic curves.

Electronics (20A and 20B). A study of the fundamental properties of electronic devices; theory of the vacuum tube as applied to industry and field communications (radio and television). Diodes, triodes, power supplies, rectifiers, and control circuits are studied.

Electronics Laboratory (20A and 20B). A laboratory course (taken simultaneously with Electronics 20A and 20B) covering electron emission, tube characteristics, amplifiers, rectifiers, thyratrons. Experiments are performed by the student.

Engineering Drawing (10A and 10B). Lettering, shop sketches, orthographic projections, use of instruments, drafting standards, details from assemblies, tracings, geometrical constructions. Application of descriptive geometry to auxiliary views, isometric and oblique drawing, revolved objects, intersecting and developed surfaces.

Engineering Laboratory (20A and 20B). Direct- and alternating-current measurements; calibration of meters; use of bridge circuits; testing and analysis of d-c and a-c machinery, transformers and apparatus; operation and testing of steam engines and equipment; refrigeration and air conditioning controls; technical reports.

English (10A and 10B). (Writing and Speaking) A discussion and practice course providing a review of the fundamental skills in written and oral English: sentence structure, grammar, punctuation, correct usage, spelling. Emphasis is on clear sentences, mature and varied sentence patterns, and good manuscript. Students practice writing acceptable sentences and paragraphs; reading and use of a library. In the second semester the fundamentals of effective practical speaking are covered: selecting a subject, organizing ideas, delivery, and voice.

English (20A and 20B). A discussion and practice course in the fundamentals of technical writing and practical speaking; organizing ideas, outlining, and writing of various types of technical reports; business correspondence. In the second semester the emphasis is on preparing and presenting speeches, formal and informal, that the technician and supervisor may be called upon to make.

Industrial Supervision (20A and 20B). Training in job management, leadership; good foundations for job relations; handling job relations problems; job instruction; planning and laying out work; waste control; safety; the supervisor's responsibilities to management, to other supervisors, and to his men. Actual cases of human relations problems in industry are studied to develop in the student the technique of working with supervisors, associates, subordinates, and the public.

Mathematics (10A and 10B). A review of computational methods and the use of the slide rule; college algebra and plane geometry with the essentials of vector algebra and simple harmonic motion. The topics are taught in such order as to be consistent from a mathematical viewpoint and at the same time supply the student with the mathematical tools needed in his engineering subjects.

Mathematics (20A and 20B). A course in elementary differential and integral calculus with emphasis on their application to engineering problems. Analytic geometry is introduced where needed to clarify the calculus.

Mechanics (10A and 10B). Definition and concept of force; mechanics of fluids (pressure, Pascal's Law, Archimedes' Principle, the atmosphere, and Boyle's Law); elements of heat (temperature and measurement, heat units, specific heat transfer, humidity, and air conditioning); statics (mathematical and graphical solution of vector problems, concurrent, parallel, and nonconcurrent forces, analysis of trusses and structures); uniform linear motion (falling bodies and projectiles); Newton's Law of Motion; work, power, and energy; basic machines. The discussion of each subject will include demonstrations and problems.

Mechanics (20A). A study of the transmission of motion by means of linkages, belts, chains; cams and their application to screw machines; gearing, types of gears, and gear trains.

Metal Laboratory (10A and 10B). This course is designed to be of immediate help to the student on his cooperative job. It consists of a familiarization course in the use and operation of machine tools with the student making a simple lathe project. The student is taught the care and use of hand tools and measuring devices of the machine shop. Part of the time is spent on simple soldering operations with sheet metal and wire, and on welding with both electric arc and oxy-acetylene. A portion of the time is devoted to foundry practice with the actual making of cores and molds from patterns. Inspection trips to local foundries are included.

Metal Laboratory (20A and 20B). This course includes both the technical knowledge and the skills necessary to operate machine tools. By making small tools the student learns various lathe operations such as straight turning, taper turning, drilling, boring, reaming, thread chasing, and knurling. The use of the milling machine includes plane milling, form milling and cutting key-ways. The use of the Do-All saw, drill press, cylindrical and surface grinders is taught. Calculations of feed and speed, use of gage blocks, sine bar and other precision measuring devices are studied. Emphasis is placed on proper routing and planning of production jobs.

Physics Laboratory (10A and 10B). Working from a laboratory manual the student will perform simple physical experiments relating to and in the same sequence with the lecture work in Mechanics 10A and 10B, and Electricity 10A and 10B. The laboratory work will consist of setting up the apparatus, making various measurements and computations, and preparing a formal written report on each experiment. Each of the following subjects will include several experiments: density and specific gravity; liquids and gases; heat; statics; uniform motion; magnetism and electricity; d-c meters and machines.

Psychology (10A and 10B). A study of the general principles of psychology from a nontechnical viewpoint, emphasis being on their usefulness in daily life, in school, on the cooperative job, and in social activities. Subjects covered are: how to learn, personality development, basic human motivation, dealing with people.

Strength of Materials (20A and 20B). Strength of Materials is the study of stresses produced within a material as well as the change of shape under applied forces. A knowledge of this subject is fundamental in design of machinery. The topics covered are the physical properties of the common materials of industry, simple stresses, yield strengths, ultimate strength, factors of safety, riveted and welded joints, design of beams, shafts, impact and repeated loads.

Technical Reading (10B). How to Read Technical Literature. A practice and discussion course designed to increase reading rate and comprehension level for selected types of writing. The course offers intensive training in skills required in the technical field and in remedial work with individuals.

The cooperative plan. Under the cooperative plan of education each student holds a job in industry at which he works during alternate periods, generally four weeks.

Analysis of Electrical Engineering Technology Curriculum

Curriculum	Total contact hours					
	Major technical specialty	Allied technical specialty	Mathematics	Lab	"General" subjects	
					English and communications	Other
Electrical Engineering Technology........	241	231	252	861	55	73
1. Chemistry.......	...	63	...	84		
2. Electricity.......	178	...	...	126		
3. Engng. Drawing..	...	21	...	147		
4. Electronics.......	63	...	...	42		
5. Engineering Lab..	...	...	...	84		
6. English & Technical Reading....	...	...	...	...	55	
7. Mathematics.....	...	...	252			
8. Mechanics.......	...	63	...	42		
9. Metal Laboratory	...	...	...	189		
10. Physics..........	...	...	...	147		
11. Psychology.......	...	...	...	...	..	21
12. Natural History ..	...	...	...	...	..	10
13. Industrial Supervision..........	...	...	...	...	..	42
14. Strength of Materials........	...	84				

Total contact hours: Class 852, Lab 861, Shop 0—Total 1713 (+ co-op work, 1920)

Curriculum in Industrial Technology

The student in Industrial Technology is trained primarily for supervisory and management positions in the manufacturing industries. However, the very nature of the broad curriculum, stressing principles and practices of scientific management, enables a graduate to compete successfully for a variety of positions. These range from almost every phase of factory planning and operation to technical sales, positions with casualty and fire insurance companies that require knowledge of industrial safety, many staff department positions with transportation, distributing, and utility companies, and the operation of private business.

First Year
FIRST QUARTER (10 Weeks)

	Class hours	Lab hours	Total hrs. (credits)
General Chemistry 111	5	0	5
Technical Drawing I	0	6	2
Industrial Technology 111 (Human Relations)	3	0	3
Technical Math 111 (Algebra)	5	0	5
Mechanical Technology 111 (Tools, Methods)	5	0	5
Total	18	6	20

SECOND QUARTER

	Class hours	Lab hours	Total hrs. (credits)
Technical Drawing II	0	6	2
Technical English 111 (Comp. & Rhet.)	3	0	3
Industrial Technology 121 (Job Evaluation)	2	0	2
Technical Math 112 (Trig., Analyt.)	5	0	5
Mechanical Technology 121 (Gn. Mtl. Shop)	0	6	2
Technical Physics 121 (Mechanics)	5	3	6
Total	15	15	20

Third Quarter

	Class hours	Lab hours	Total hrs. (credits)
Technical English 112 (Comp. & Rhet.)	3	0	3
Industrial Technology 122 (Ind. Accounting)	1	3	2
Industrial Technology 131 (Methods Imprvt.)	3	0	3
Industrial Technology 151 (Ind. Safety)	3	0	3
Mechanical Technology 122 (Machine Shop)	0	6	2
Technical Physics 122 (Electricity)	5	3	6
Total	15	12	19

Second Year

Fourth Quarter

Technical English 221 (Public Speaking)	3	0	3
Industrial Technology 223 (Ind. Economics)	5	0	5
Industrial Technology 232 (Motion Time Study)	2	3	3
Industrial Technology 233 (Mat'ls Handling)	2	0	2
Industrial Technology 234 (Prod. Control)	3	0	3
Technical Physics 123 (Heat, Sound, Light)	3	3	4
Total	18	6	20

Fifth Quarter

Technical Drawing 221 (Mach. Sketching)	0	6	2
Technical English 231 (Tech. Writing)	3	0	3
Industrial Technology 212 (Labor Relations)	2	0	2
Industrial Technology 224 (Wage Incentives)	2	0	2
Industrial Technology 235 (Quality Control)	2	0	2
Industrial Technology 241 (Ind. Sales & Pur.)	2	0	2
Industrial Technology 242 (Small Bus. Mgt.)	3	0	3
Mechanical Technology 214 (Inspec. Methods)	3	0	3
Total	17	6	19

SIXTH QUARTER

	Class hours	Lab hours	Total hrs. (credits)
Industrial Technology 213 (Supv. Training)	5	0	5
Industrial Technology 225 (Cost Control)	2	0	2
Industrial Technology 236 (Plant Layout)	2	3	3
Industrial Technology 237 (Ind. Analy.)	0	6	2
Industrial Technology 243 (Business Law)	3	0	3
Industrial Technology 261 (Seminar)	1	0	1
Mechanical Technology 215 (Jigs and Fixtures)	2	3	3
Total	15	12	19

Course descriptions

General Chemistry (111). A survey of general chemistry with the emphasis on inorganic. Numerous classroom demonstrations are used to illustrate principles studied. Text: Arnold J. Currier and Arthur Rose, *General and Applied Chemistry,* McGraw-Hill Book Company, Inc., New York, 1948.

Technical Drawing I (111). Introduction to drawing, use of instruments, lettering, geometric construction, orthographic projection, auxiliary views, dimensioning, and drawing conventions. Text: Thomas E. French and Charles J. Vierck, *A Manual of Engineering Drawing for Students and Draftsmen,* 8th ed., McGraw-Hill Book Company, Inc., New York, 1953.

Industrial Technology—Human Relations (111). Training in development of personality, ability to analyze problems involving human relations, and the development of good foundations for personnel relations. Actual cases of human relations problems in industry are studied with a view toward developing the technique of working with superiors, associates, and subordinates. Text: Auren Uris and Betty Shapin, *Working with People,* The Macmillan Company, New York, 1949.

Technical Math—Algebra (111). (Prerequisite: Two units of high school algebra or Technical Math 10.) Fundamental operations in algebra, factoring, fractions, exponents, radicals, complex numbers, linear equations, systems of linear equations, determinants, quadratic equations, quadratic systems in two unknowns, ratio, proportion and variation, graphical solution of simultaneous equations, and logarithms. Text: H. K. Fulmer and W. Reynolds, *College Algebra*, Ginn & Company, Boston, 1951.

Mechanical Technology—Tools and Methods (111). An introduction to the field of metal work and industrial manufacturing for mechanical and industrial students. Possibilities and limitations of various machine tools are developed so that the student will have a basic perspective of modern efficient industrial procedure. The characteristics of different materials are covered as well as their adaptability to the various processes. Each process is covered from a technical viewpoint. Correct terms are introduced so that the student will be able to use the language of the engineer or the technician. Text: M. L. Begeman, *Manufacturing Processes*, 3d ed., John Wiley & Sons, Inc., New York, 1952.

Technical Drawing II (112). (Prerequisite: Technical Drawing I.) Continuation of topics introduced in Technical Drawing I, plus threads and fasteners, sectioning, conventional representation, working drawings, and ink tracings. Text: Same as Technical Drawing I.

Technical English—Composition and Rhetoric (111). Grammar study and drill, punctuation, correct usage, sentence structure, elimination of errors in sentence structure, and writing for comprehension. Texts: John C. Hodges, *Harbrace College Workbook*, Harcourt, Brace and Company, Inc., New York; P. S. Grant and W. C. Foreman, *Exercises in Writing and Thinking*, Houghton Mifflin Company, Boston, 1952; *American College Dictionary*, Random House, New York.

Industrial Technology—Job Evaluation (121). A study of the techniques and principles of job analysis and evaluation as a means for developing sound wage and salary administration. Text: R. C. Smyth and M. J. Murphy, *Job Evaluation and Employee Rating*, McGraw-Hill Book Company, Inc., New York, 1946.

Technical Mathematics—Applied Trigonometry and Analytic Geometry (112). (Prerequisite: Technical Math 111.) Trigonometric functions, plane right triangles, reduction formulas, fundamental relations, addition formulas, double angles, half angles, inverse functions, and solution of oblique triangles. Approximately two-thirds of the quarter is devoted to topics in trigonometry. During the remainder of the quarter topics in analytics are considered. Rectangular coordinate systems, locus and equations, the straight line, the circle, the parabola, and the hyperbola are the topics covered. Text: E. Richard Heineman, *Plane Trigonometry*, 2d ed., McGraw-Hill Book Company, Inc., New York, 1956.

Mechanical Technology—General Metal Shop (121). An introduction to metal work, giving the students both actual practice and related information in lathe work, bench metal, acetylene welding and cutting, and forging. The proper use and care of hand tools are stressed along with maintenance of shop equipment. Lectures are given on the most frequently used hand tools, measuring devices, and specifications of ordering materials and supplies. Text: Henry Ford Trade School, *Shop Theory*, McGraw-Hill Book Company, Inc., New York, 1955.

Physics—Mechanics (121). (Prerequisite or concurrently: Technical Math 112.) An introduction to Newtonian mechanics. Subject matter includes measurement, coplanar concurrent forces, coplanar parallel forces, forces in space, work and energy, simple machines, accelerated motion, friction, vibratory motion, rotary motion, gravitation, fluids in motion, elasticity and strength of materials. Laboratory exercises parallel the work in the classroom. Text: O. H. Blackwood and W. Kelly, *General Physics*, 2d ed., John Wiley & Sons, Inc., New York, 1955, and Defore, Clark, and Crawford, *Physics Laboratory Exercises*, 2d ed.

Technical English—Composition and Rhetoric (112). (Prerequisite: Technical English 111.) Vocabulary building, dictionary study, practice in developing sentence style, precise writing, paragraph technique, and business correspondence. Text: Same as Technical English 111 and Robert L. Shurter, *Effective Letters in Business*, 2d ed., McGraw-Hill Book Company, Inc., New York, 1954.

Industrial Technology—Industrial Accounting (122). A course designed to give the student a sound foundation in general accounting principles, familiarization with cost accounting theory and practices, and a working knowledge of the use of accounting data and its relationship to industrial management. Text: Samuel Specthrie, *Industrial Accounting: Brief Course and Workbook*, Prentice-Hall, Inc., Englewood Cliffs, N.J.

Industrial Technology—Methods Improvement (131). Study of the various production methods, batch and mass production techniques; practice in writing standard procedures, raw material specifications, and manufacturing instructions. The application of the "questioning attitude" in the search for better manufacturing methods and job procedures and the four-step method of job improvement are also studied. Text: Marvin E. Mundel, *Motion and Time Study Principles and Practice*, 5th ed., Prentice-Hall, Inc., Englewood Cliffs, N.J., 1955, Alex F. Osborn, *Applied Imagination*, rev. ed., Charles Scribner's Sons, New York, 1953.

Industrial Technology—Industrial Safety (151). A basic study of industrial accident prevention, considering the nature and extent of the accident problem. A practical study is given the technique for control of industrial hazards together with the fundamentals of good organization. Text: Roland P. Blake, *Industrial Safety*, 2d ed., Prentice-Hall, Inc., Englewood Cliffs, N.J., 1953.

Mechanical Technology—Machine Shop I (122). (Prerequisite: T. Dr. 111.) Fundamental machine operations of drilling, reaming, turning between centers, check work, thread cutting, shaper work, layout, and finishing. Special attention will be given to cutting speeds, tools and drill grinding, and machine upkeep. Text: John T. Shuman, *Machine Shop Work*, American Technical Society, Chicago, 1942.

Technical Physics—Electricity (122). An introduction to electricity and a study of its simpler applications. The subject matter includes magnetism, electrostatics, potential differences, work and power in electrical circuits, Joule's law, resistance in series and parallel, Ohm's law, electrochemical effects, motors, generators, induced electromotive forces, Lenz's law, electromagnetic effects, electrical measuring, high frequency oscillations. The laboratory work parallels the work in the classroom. Text: Same as for Technical Physics 121.

Technical English—Public Speaking (221). (Prerequisite: Technical English 112.) Study and practice in the fundamentals of public speaking. The subject includes training in selecting a subject, obtaining and organizing material, and presenting speeches effectively. Each student makes several speeches before an audience. Text: Allan H. Monroe, *Principles of Speech*, Scott, Foresman and Company, Chicago, 1951.

Industrial Technology—Industrial Economics (223). Output and life of equipment, operation costs, depreciation rates, economic selection of equipment, determination of economic lot sizes, and cost studies on representative problems. Text: E. L. Grant, *Principles of Engineering Economy*, 3d ed., The Ronald Press Company, New York, 1950.

Industrial Technology—Motion and Time Study (232). (Prerequisite: Industrial Technology 131.) Principles of motion economy, tools for motion study, time-study methods and practice; standard data and formula construction; use of methods-time measurements as a substitute for time studies. Text: Marvin E. Mundel, *Motion and Time Study Principles and Practice*, 5th ed., Prentice-Hall, Inc., Englewood Cliffs, N.J., 1955.

Industrial Technology—Materials Handling (223). Selection and use of modern equipment and methods for handling material in the industrial processes. Text: I. M. Footlik and J. F. Carle, *Industrial Materials Handling,* Lincoln Extension Institute, Cleveland, Ohio.

Industrial Technology—Production Control (234). (Prerequisite: Industrial Technology 131.) The preparation for production, planning based on sales forecasts, operation sheets, routing, scheduling, dispatching, follow-up, inventory control, receiving, stores and shipping, control forms and reports. Text: E. H. McNiece, *Production Forecasting, Planning, and Control,* John Wiley & Sons, Inc., New York, 1951.

Technical Physics—Heat, Sound, Light (123). (Prerequisite: Technical Physics 121.) The elementary principles of heat, sound, and light and their technical applications. Class work includes discussions of temperature and its measurement, thermal expansion, heat units, work and heat, transfer of heat, change of state, meteorology, heat engines, wave motion, sound, propagation of light, photometry, reflection, refraction, spectra, color, and optical instruments. Laboratory exercises parallel the work in the classroom. Text: Same as for Technical Physics 121.

Technical Drawing—Machine Sketching (221). (Prerequisite: Technical Drawing 112.) A step-by-step procedure in freehand sketching of machine parts with pencil. Sketches are made in orthographic, isometric, and oblique projection, as well as in true perspective. Dimensioning and shading of sketches are included. Text: Same as Technical Drawing 111 and 112.

Technical English—Technical Writing (231). (Prerequisite: Technical English 112.) Study of the fundamentals of technical writing style and mechanics with practice in preparing reports of the various types most likely to be used on the job by technicians. Text: Carl G. Gaum and others, *Report Writing,* 3d ed., Prentice-Hall, Inc., Englewood Cliffs, N.J., 1950. Selected reports from industrial organizations.

Industrial Technology—Labor Relations (212). (Prerequisite: Industrial Technology 111.) Personnel policies, selection and employment, interviewing and testing, employee records, training, employee benefits, collective bargaining and employer-employee relations, grievance procedure, wage and salary standards, and use of practical industrial psychology. Text: Walter D. Scott, Robert C. Clothier, and William R. Spriegel, *Personnel Management,* 5th ed., McGraw-Hill Book Company, Inc., New York, 1954; Malin and Unterberger, *The Taft-Hartley Act in Operation.*

Industrial Technology—Wage Incentives (224). (Prerequisite: Industrial Technology 131.) Basic requirements of a sound wage incentive plan, control of quality in incentive installations, union participation. Subject matter includes a study of five types of wage incentive plans. Text: J. K. Louden, *Wage Incentives,* John Wiley & Sons, Inc., New York, 1944.

Industrial Technology—Quality Control (235). Principles of inspection and quality control, with special emphasis on setting up, maintaining, and interpreting statistical control charts. Text: W. B. Rice, *Control Charts in Factory Management,* John Wiley & Sons, Inc., New York, 1947.

Industrial Technology—Industrial Sales and Purchasing (241). Methods and principles of industrial sales and service engineering as encountered in the basic industries; the nature of the purchasing function, including the art of the interview and conference, sources of purchasing information, forecasting ultimate values, and reciprocity purchasing. Text: B. Lester, *Sales Engineering,* 2d ed., John Wiley & Sons, Inc., New York, 1950.

Industrial Technology—Small Business Management (242). (Prerequisite: Industrial Technology 122.) Training in the operation of a small business concern including a practical knowledge of accepted accounting procedures, order billing, credits and collections, costs, payroll procedures, taxes, and information about standard business and office machines. Text: Pearce C. Kelly and Kenneth Lawyer, *How to Organize and Operate a Small Business,* 2d ed., Prentice-Hall, Inc., New York, 1955.

Mechanical Technology—Inspection Methods (214). (Prerequisite: Mechanical Technology 121 and 122.) A study of the use and care of precision instruments and methods of inspection. Types and methods of inspection are compared and discussed from samples chosen from industry as a comparison. Text: Leno Michelon, *Industrial Inspection Methods,* rev. ed., Harper & Brothers, New York, 1950.

Industrial Technology—Supervisory Training (213). Line of responsibility and authority, technique of job instruction, personal leadership, technique of conducting a conference, how to produce for a profit. The subject treats problems of the supervisor as cost man, as safety man, as production man, as quality man, as personnel man, as the manager of his department. Text: Carl Heyel, *The Foreman's Handbook,* 3d ed., McGraw-Hill Book Company, Inc., New York, 1955.

Industrial Technology—Cost Control (225). (Prerequisite: Industrial Technology 122 and 242.) Control of material and labor costs, determination of labor requirements, cost studies for use in estimating product prices. Text: James H. March, *Cost Accounting,* McGraw-Hill Book Company, Inc., New York, 1949.

Industrial Technology—Plant Layout (236). (Prerequisite: Mechanical Technology 122, Industrial Technology 233, Industrial Technology 121.) Principles of plant layout, process and flow charts, tools and aids for effective plant layouts, case studies; the supervisor's responsibility for building and equipment maintenance. Text: J. M. Apple, *Plant Layout and Materials Handling* and *Lab Manual for Plant Layout,* The Ronald Press Company, New York, 1950.

Industrial Technology—Industry Analysis (237). A survey and study of the various fields of industrial activity such as textile, steel, chemical, wood products, food processing, and mechanical assembly. Field trips and detailed reports will be included in order to enable the student to make a better choice of the particular type of industry he desires to enter.

Industrial Technology—Business Law (243). The general laws of contracts, agency, sales agreements, and engineering

Analysis of Industrial Technology Curriculum

| Curriculum | Total contact hours | | | | | |
| | Major technical specialty | Allied technical specialty | Mathematics | Lab | "General" subjects | |
					English and communications	Other
Industrial Technology	400	300	100	570	90	30
1. Chemistry & Physics..........	...	130	...	90		
2. Drawing.........	...	...	...	180		
3. Human Relations.	...	...	...	...	..	30
4. Mathematics.....	...	...	100			
5. ME Tech. subjects	...	170	...	180		
6. English & Report Writing, etc......	...	...	...	...	90	
7. Job Evaluation...	20					
8. Accounting & Cost Control Analysis; Purchasing & Sales	50	...	...	90		
9. Methods.........	30					
10. Industrial Safety..	30					
11. Plant Layout.....	20	...	...	30		
12. Motion & Time Study..........	20					
13. Mtls. Handling...	20					
14. Prod. & Qual. Control..........	50					
15. Management-Labor Relations-Supv., etc......	160					

Total contact hours: Class 920, Lab 570—Total 1490

specifications as incorporated into contracts; the business, legal and ethical phases of engineering. Text: Charles, *College Law;* Charles, *Study Reports for College Law.*

Industrial Technology—Seminar (261). A study of the techniques for obtaining employment, improving one's position after he gets the job, and a general discussion of professional ethics. Lecture notes, visiting specialists.

Mechanical Technology—Jigs and Fixtures (215). (Prerequisite: Mechanical Technology 121 and 122.) Factors involved in large quantity production machine processes. Types of jobs and fixtures, different methods of gaging work, ease of operation, and methods of assembly are studied. Machine parts are selected and preliminary methods of production together with cost estimates and production costs are calculated for each part chosen. Text: Franklin D. Jones, *Jig and Fixture Design,* The Industrial Press, New York.

Curriculum in Machine Construction and Tool Design

A comprehensive training is offered to the young man who wishes to develop to maximum capacity his opportunities for a career as an engineering technician in the mechanical field. The opportunities are varied and interesting. Graduates readily find employment as laboratory technicians, engineering assistants, mechanical draftsmen, inspectors, estimators, expediters, salesmen of mechanical equipment, and other positions in production and maintenance. The broad and thorough training provided in this course has enabled many men to attain positions of high responsibility. Tool designers, engineers, and superintendents are listed among the alumni.

Course descriptions

Mechanical Drawing (401). This course is planned to give the student a thorough training in the fundamental principles of engineering drawing. Basic instruction is given in the care and use of drawing instruments and equipment, simplified geometrical constructions, technical lettering, fundamental prin-

First Year

FIRST SEMESTER

	Hours per week		
	Class	Lab	Credit
Mechanical Drawing (401)	0	5	2
Algebra & Trigonometry (405)	4	0	4
Physics (407)	3	2	4
English Composition (409)	3	0	3
Electricity (413)	3	0	3
Electrical Laboratory (415)	0	2	1
Pattern Making (417)	0	2	1
Welding (419)	0	2	1
Casting Processes (421)	0	2	1
Total	13	15	20

SECOND SEMESTER

Mechanical Drawing (402)	0	5	2
Machine Shop Practice (404)	1	2	2
Algebra & Trigonometry (406)	4	0	4
Physics (408)	3	2	4
Oral Communication (410)	2	0	2
Electricity (414)	3	0	3
Electrical Laboratory (416)	0	2	1
Welding (420)	0	2	1
Casting Processes (422)	0	2	1
Total	13	15	20

Summer Reading (credit required for graduation) (430)

Second Year

FIRST SEMESTER

Mechanical Design (451)	4	5	6
Machine Shop Practice (453)	0	6	3
Introduction to Calculus (455)	3	0	3
Electrical Machinery (457)	3	0	3
Electrical Machinery Laboratory (459)	0	2	1
Diesel Engines (461)	3	0	3
Diesel Engine Laboratory (463)	0	2	1
Total	13	15	20

SECOND SEMESTER

	Hours per week		
	Class	Lab	Credit
Machine & Tool Design (452)	4	5	6
Machine Shop Practice (454)	0	6	3
Analytical Geometry &			
Mathematical Analysis (456)	2	0	2
Heat (458)	3	0	3
Heat Laboratory (460)	0	3	1
Strength of Materials (466)	3	2	4
Total	12	16	19

ciples of projection, selection of views, drafting room standards and conventions, rules of dimensioning applied to working drawings of machine parts, use of auxiliary views and conventions of sectioning.

Mechanical Drawing (402). This is a continuation of Subject 401 and includes isometric drawing, intersections, and developments; pen and ink tracings and methods of production of drawings; screw fastenings, and threaded parts; freehand sketches of measured machine parts; detail and assembly drawings of simple machines.

Machine Shop Practice (404). Practical experience is obtained in bench work, including chipping, filing, layout, drilling, tapping and thread cutting with dies; the use of measuring tools; the heat treatment of small tools; and simple lathe work.

Algebra and Trigonometry (405). A post-secondary study of arithmetic is made with emphasis on its role as a tool for rapid and efficient methods of calculation. Instruction is given in the more effective use of mathematical tables, slide rule, graphical solutions, and other aids to computation. The following additional topics are studied: the numerical trigonometry of the right triangle; algebra, including the fundamental processes, formula manipulation and solution of linear equations, especially in relation to practical applications; analytical geometry of the straight line; and simultaneous linear equations, including solution by determinants and by graphical means.

Algebra and Trigonometry (406). This is a course in college algebra and trigonometry, in which emphasis is placed on practical problems pertaining to the student's principal field of interest. The topics studied are quadratic equations; ratio, proportion, variation, common and natural logarithms; complex numbers and vector representation; trigonometry, including properties of the trigonometric functions, trigonometric identities and equations; radian measure; and the solution of the oblique triangle.

Physics (407). Since the fundamentals of physics are the foundation for all technical education, a thorough study of the basic principles of this science is required. The course covers the following major areas and topics: Heat and fluids, which include temperature, specific heat, properties of gases, latent heat, heat transfer, fluid pressure, density, buoyancy, and hydraulics; sound and light, which include wave motion, velocity, physics of musical sound, illumination, reflection, refraction, diffraction, and lenses. Some attention is given to the newer physical science topics.

Physics (408). This is a continuation of Physics 407 and consists of a thorough study of the following major areas and topics in mechanics: Statics, including composition and resolution of forces, equilibrium, concurrent forces, parallel forces, center of gravity, nonconcurrent forces; and dynamics, including friction, elasticity, motion, acceleration, forces producing motion, moment of inertia, work, power, and energy.

English Composition (409). This is a course in written communication, including consideration of the techniques of writing with emphasis on exposition. Technical consideration of sentences, paragraph structure, and construction of the whole theme involving the collection and logical handling of material are stressed. Attention is given to instruction in the basic principles of business letter writing, with particular emphasis being placed on the letter of application.

Oral Communications (410). This is a practical treatment of the principles and methods required in a brief course in public speaking. The student practices the essentials of selecting the subject, finding the material, achieving clarity, organizing and outlining, developing interest and delivery.

Electricity (413). A study is made of direct current circuits and machines which includes series, parallel, and series-parallel circuits; power calculations; use of electrical measuring instruments; measurement of resistance by the voltmeter-ammeter and Wheatstone Bridge methods; properties of wire; efficiency of distribution systems; permanent and electromagnets; series and parallel magnetic circuits; calculation of flux densities and magnetomotive force; construction, operation, and performance characteristics of series, shunt, and compound generators and motors; voltage regulation and control of d-c generators; methods of motor speed control.

Electricity (414). This is a continuation of Subject 413 with advanced work on d-c generators and motors which includes parallel operation and load-division of compound generators; speed-torque relations and the proper selection and application of series, shunt, and compound motors; efficiency from losses and brake horsepower tests. Students also become familiar with the generation of an alternating voltage of sine wave form; use of vectors; calculation and vector solution of current, voltage and power relations in series, parallel, and series-parallel a-c circuits; calculations for impedance, reactance, inductance, effective resistance, power and power factor.

Electrical Laboratory (415). Laboratory work consists of use of electrical measuring instruments; determination of current and voltage in series, parallel, and series-parallel circuits; measurement of resistance by the voltmeter-ammeter and Wheatstone Bridge methods; voltage drop in, and the efficiency of, distributing systems; calibration of voltmeters and ammeters by the comparison method; study, adjustment, and calibration of direct current watt-hour meters; study of the construction of the dynamo with measurements of the resistance of armature, interpole, series, and shunt field circuits; building up a generator; standard tests on shunt and compound generators to determine their operating characteristics. Written reports are required.

Electrical Laboratory (416). The laboratory work in this course parallels the classroom work of Subject 414 and includes parallel operation and load division of compound generators, speed-torque and static-torque tests on series, shunt and compound motors; stray-power method of determining efficiency; current and voltage relations in series and parallel a-c circuits; measurement of power and power factor; determination of effective resistance, impedance, reactance inductance. Written reports are required.

Pattern Making (417). Instruction is given in the care and use of woodworking tools and machines, correct use of materials used in pattern construction; characteristics, trade names, and uses of the various metals used in pattern making and foundry work, metal shrinkages and rules used to compensate for shrinkage; machine shop requirements in pattern making; relationship between drafting rooms, pattern shops, foundries, and machine shops; shop talks and demonstrations relating to the construction of complicated patterns and the methods used for high production of castings.

Welding (419). Instruction is given in the setup and safe operation of oxy-acetylene welding apparatus. Practice is obtained in welding pipe and various sheet-metal joints. Cast iron and bronze are also welded and brazed. Demonstrations are given of the application of silver brazing alloys, aluminum welding and brazing. Students prepare joints by both hand and machine cutting with the oxy-acetylene torch. Practice is also given in arc-welding using a-c transformer and d-c motor generators welding machines. A study is made of the correct welding heats, polarities, and electrodes to use when welding various materials and alloys. Fillet and butt joints are welded and tested. Demonstrations are given of both spot and inert-gas-shielded arc-welding.

Welding (420). Through instruction and practice, students in this advanced course obtain considerable skill in the welding of various fillet and butt joints as well as sheet-metal joints in both the flat and vertical positions using both oxy-acetylene and arc-welding equipment. Students must acquire the ability to satisfactorily deposit beads and weaves to make sound joints. The study of welding heats, polarities, and electrodes suitable for the arc-welding of various alloys is continued, and the special problems caused by unusual shapes and forms are analyzed. Practice is given in the welding and brazing of cast iron and bronze and the welding of aluminum. Demonstrations are given of the techniques used in atomic-hydrogen welding and in the forging and tempering of tools.

Casting Processes (421). This is a study of the application of the casting processes to the economical design and manufacture of components used in the machine industry. Instruction is given in the fundamental molding, coremaking, melting and pouring operations necessary to produce castings or iron, bronze, and aluminum alloys. The elementary metallurgy of ferrous and nonferrous metals is covered, including the selection of alloys for specific purposes, effect of various commonly used alloying elements, shrinkage and solidification of metals and alloys, casting defects and their causes, and the advantages of cast metals over other forms of fabrication.

Casting Processes (422). A study of the metallurgy of the foundry is made, including the structure of iron, steel, and malleable iron, rate of cooling and its effect on grain structure, gates and risers, crystallization of metals, cast weld construction, casting defects, inspection of castings and applications of alloys to ferrous and nonferrous metals. The mounting of patterns on match plates for bench and machine molding is discussed. The more difficult types of molds are made and castings produced. Cores are made by both hand and machine methods.

Summer Reading (430). During the summer vacations between their first and second years, all students are required to

take a prescribed course of selected reading which will be subject to examination during the fall term of the second year.

Mechanical Design (451). The drawings made in this course
are selected to emphasize to the student designer the proper
methods of constructing machine parts and the correct specifications of materials and manufacturing processes. The work
consists of making layouts of gear tooth forms, making shop
drawings of spur, bevel, helical, and worm gears, studying
methods of cutting various gear-tooth forms, and making layouts of cams and other mechanisms. A study of the elements
of mechanisms is included to enable students to apply the
fundamental principles of kinematics to the design of mechanical movements.

Machine and Tool Design (452). The problems assigned to
students in this course include the design and jigs and fixtures
for finishing interchangeable machine parts, design of small
tools and cutters, explanation of punch and die work, elements
of machine design, practical application of the principles of
mechanisms and strength of materials, study of data and information found in handbooks and machine design texts, and
the application of such information to the problems in design.
Many elementary problems in the design of machine parts are
included.

Machine Shop Practice (453–454). Practical experience is
gained by doing advanced machine work on lathes, milling
machines, shapers, and grinders; calculating, cutting, and measuring gears; using precision measuring tools and checking instruments in a well-equipped measuring room. Demonstrations
are given to acquaint the student with hardness testing equipment and the heat treatment of various metals.

Introduction to Calculus (455). An introductory course is
given in calculus, including the following topics: graphical integration and estimation of mean values, empirical equations,
graphical estimation of rates, introduction to elementary differential calculus utilizing practical problems involving rates
of change and maximum and minimum values, elementary

integration and the calculation of areas, volumes, work, water pressure, etc.

Analytical Geometry and Mathematical Analysis (456). The topics covered in this course are as follows: binomial theorem, progressions, analytical geometry of the conic sections, curve sketching, polar coordinates, parameters, translation and rotation of axes, tangents and normals, and analytical geometry of solid figures.

Electrical Machinery (457). The topics covered in this course include current and voltage relations in delta and Y connected circuits; measurement of polyphase power by the two- and three-wattmeter methods; calculation of power and power factor; construction, operation and performance characteristics of alternators; synchronizing and load division; load tests and efficiency of transformers from their losses; single and polyphase induction motors and their performance characteristics.

Heat (458). A study is made of the fundamental laws of heat, properties of saturated and superheated vapors, steam and vapor processes and their application to prime movers; power and efficiency calculations for boilers, engines, turbines and pumps; use of steam and other tables; and modern power cycles.

Electrical Machinery Laboratory (459). This laboratory course includes measurement of current and voltage in delta and Y connected circuits; power measurements in delta and Y connected circuits by the two- and three-wattmeter methods; load tests and voltage regulation of alternators; synchronizing and load division of alternators; transformer connections and efficiency from their losses; load tests on single and polyphase induction motors; operation of the synchronous motor. Written reports are required.

Heat Laboratory (460). The laboratory work parallels the class work and includes the operation and testing of boilers, engines, and pumps, and other auxiliary apparatus; and the study of valves, fittings, gages, and other equipment. The

Analysis of Curriculum in Machine Construction and Tool Design

Curriculum	Total contact hours					
	Major technical specialty	Allied technical specialty	Mathematics	Shop	Lab	"General" subjects (English and communications)
Machine Construction and Tool Design....	324	270	234	252	846	108
1. Mechanical Drawing.........	...	...	...	...	180	
2. Algebra & Trigonometry.....	...	...	144			
3. Physics..........	...	108	...	...	72	
4. English Composition......	...	...	...	...	...	54
5. Oral Composition.	...	...	...	...	...	54
6. Electricity........	...	108	...	...	72	
7. Machine Shop Practice.	18	...	...	252		
8. Pattern Making...	...	...	...	...	36	
9. Welding.........	...	...	...	...	72	
10. Casting Processes..	...	...	...	...	72	
11. Mechanical Design	72	...	...	...	90	
12. Machine & Tool Design...........	72	...	...	...	90	
13. Intro. to Calculus	...	...	54			
14. Analytic Geometry & Math. Analysis..	...	...	36			
15. Electrical Machinery.......	...	54	...	...	36	
16. Heat............	54	...	...	...	54	
17. Diesel Engines....	54	...	...	...	36	
18. Strength of Materials........	54	...	...	...	36	

Total contact hours: Class 936, Lab 846, Shop 252—Total 2034

calorific determination and other tests of solid and liquid fuels are conducted, as well as water and gas analysis experiments.

Diesel Engines (461). A study is made of the laws and processes of perfect gases, the ideal cycles as applied to the internal combustion engine and the use of the pressure-volume and temperature-entropy planes. The actual cycles and performance of the Otto and diesel engines are studied along with calculations of horsepower and efficiencies. Applications of the internal combustion engine are discussed. The elementary cycle for the gas turbine is studied, along with the compression and expansion of air.

Diesel Engine Laboratory (463). Laboratory work consists of studies of two- and four-stroke cycle engines such as the General Motors, Superior, Buda, and Caterpillar engines. Fuel and lubricating oils are tested as to flash and fire point and viscosity. Several efficiency and economy tests are made of the component parts of the diesel engine, such as the injection system and governing system.

Strength of Materials (466). This course includes a study of fundamental stress and strain relationships. Stresses in thin-walled cylinders, and in riveted and welded joints, are studied. Shear and bending moment diagrams and the investigation of beams for shear, bending, and deflection are also included. The study of torsion, column action, and eccentrically applied loads is covered, along with fatigue, impact, and repeated stresses. The laboratory portion of the course consists of tests and written reports prepared by the student in order that he may better understand the above fundamentals.

Appendix 4. Comparison of emphasis in major division of subject matter for various typical curriculums

(Summary of Appendix 3)

Curriculums	Total	Contact hours											
		Major technical specialty		Allied* technical specialty		Mathematics		Drafting, shop, and lab		"General" subjects			
										English communications		Other	
		Hours	%	Hours	%	Hours	%	Hours	%	Hours	%	Hours	%
(A) Industrial Electronics Technology	2430	655	27	515	21	170	7	990	41	100	4	0	0
(B) Structural Design Technology	1680	276	16	312	19	132	8	816	49	72	4	72	4
(C) Electrical Engineering Technology	1713	241	14	231	14	252	15	861	50	55	3	73	4
(D) Industrial Engineering Technology	1490	400	27	300	20	100	7	570	38	90	6	30	2
(E) Mechanical Engineering Technology—Machine Construction and Tool Design	2034	324	16	270	13	234	12	1098†	54	108	5	0	0

* Includes basic sciences.
† Includes 846 lab and 252 shop.

Appendix 5. Check list of criteria for identifying technical jobs*

Classification
Technical   _____
Subtechnical _____
Trade   _____
Professional _____

Job title _____

A technical job: Low   High

1. Emphasizes technical knowledge 1 2 3 4 5
2. Emphasizes technical skill (the ability to use technical knowledge) 1 2 3 4 5
3. Deals with rational processes as contrasted with empirical rules 1 2 3 4 5
4. Has concern with cause and effect 1 2 3 4 5
5. Emphasizes analysis and diagnosis 1 2 3 4 5
6. Requires frequent exercise of ability to use involved judgment 1 2 3 4 5
7. Deals with many factors and a large number of variables 1 2 3 4 5
8. Contends with a large variety of situations 1 2 3 4 5
9. Requires a knowledge of skilled work but not necessarily skill in doing it 1 2 3 4 5
10. Requires a broad background of fundamental science and mathematics 1 2 3 4 5
11. Involves use of a variety of instruments 1 2 3 4 5
12. Requires effective use of language to interpret orders and make reports 1 2 3 4 5
13. Involves the element of leadership in supervisory occupations 1 2 3 4 5

* J. Cayce Morrison, chairman, "*A Guide to the Development of Programs for the Institutes of Applied Arts and Sciences,* The University of the State of New York, Albany, 1946.

A technical job: Low   High

14. Requires understanding of industrial equipment and
    processes 1 2 3 4 5
15. Frequently involves visualization of plans and draw-
    ings and a degree of creative design 1 2 3 4 5

For each criterion circle the number you judge to represent the degree the job requires: 1—low; 5—high. Omit those criteria which are not applicable. An average score above 3 would indicate a technical job; below 3 a trade or subtechnical job. Technical jobs which usually require four years or more of formal education should be classified as professional.

Appendix 6. Data from follow-up surveys of graduates of typical technical institute curriculums

These several representative exhibits supplement the text references in Chapter 9, "The Engineering Technician and His Employment."

A. Actual occupational titles under which the 1955, 1956, and 1957 graduates of The Pennsylvania State University technical institute curriculums in Drafting and Design Technology and Electrical Technology were employed as of 1958.

Acoustical Technician
Application Engineer
Assistant Electrical Engineer
Assistant Engineer
Assistant Research Engineer
Associate Designer
Associate Engineer

Checker
Chief Draftsman
Chief Tool Designer
Class C. Design Engineer
Computer Inspector
Customer Engineer

Design Draftsman
Design Engineer
Draftsman
Draftsman B

Electrical Designer
Electrical Draftsman
Electrical Inspector

Electrical Technician
Electronics Technician
Engineer
Engineering Aide
Engineering Assistant
Engineering Draftsman
Engineering Technician
Estimating Engineer

Field Engineer
First Class Controlman

Inspector

Junior Bridge Designer
Junior Design Engineer
Junior Draftsman
Junior Maintenance Engineer
Junior Research Engineer

Laboratory Technician
Layout Draftsman
Layout Man

Machine Designer
Mechanical Designer
Methods Analyst
Methods Engineer

Product Engineer
Project Engineer
Proposition Engineer

Quality Control Engineer
Quality Control Tester

Reactor Operator
Research Analyst
Research Assistant
Research Technician
Roll Draftsman

Sales Engineer
Senior Research Analyst
Service Engineer
Site Technician
Special Tester
Stress Analyst
Structural Steel Detail Draftsman
Supervisor

Technical Aide
Technical Assistant
Technician
Test Engineer
Time Study Observer
Tool Designer

B. *Representative first jobs and 1957 jobs for a group of typical engineering technicians graduated in Chemistry 1927–1956
by Rochester Institute of Technology.*

FIRST JOB*   PRESENT JOB*

6 to 10 years since graduation (Classes of 1947 to 1951)

Remained with same company

Asst. Lab Technician
Chemist
Lab Technician
Metallurgist
Lab Technician
Chemical Lab Assistant
Draftsman
Materials Lab Technician

Photographic Engineer
Group Leader, Organic Finishing
Senior Lab Technician
Organic Finishing Chemist II
Senior Lab Technician
Chemist
Lab Technician
Production Engineer

* The first job and present job reported in sections B, C, and D
are for the same individual in each case. That is, the individual who
reported his first job as being an "Assistant Lab Technician" also
reported that his present job was "Photographic Engineer."

FIRST JOB*	PRESENT JOB*

Transferred to different company

Chemist	Field Foreman
Control Chemist	Chemist
Lab Technician	Development Chemist

16 to 25 years since graduation (Classes of 1932 to 1941)

Remained with same company

Chemist	Chemical Engineer
Control Lab Technician	Technical Sales
Chemist	Chief Project Engineer
Lab Technician 3rd Class	Senior Chemist
Lab Technician	Senior Metallurgist
Pulp Tester	Group Leader—Physical Testing

Transferred to a different company

Chemist	General Lab Foreman
Chemist	Asst. Chief Chemist
Control Chemist	Project Engineer
Shift Chemist	Textile Chemist
Chemist	Shift Foreman
Tester and Inspector	Brewing Chemist
Technician	Research Assistant
Lab Assistant	Shift Foreman

C. Representative first jobs and 1957 jobs for a group of typical engineering technicians graduated in Electrical Technology 1927–1956 by Rochester Institute of Technology.

FIRST JOB*	PRESENT JOB*

6 to 10 years since graduation (Classes of 1947 to 1951)

Remained with same company

| Electrician | Automotive Technician |
| Relay Adjuster | Application Engineer |

* The first job and present job reported in sections B, C, and D are for the same individual in each case. That is, the individual who reported his first job as being an "Assistant Lab Technician" also reported that his present job was "Photographic Engineer."

FIRST JOB*	PRESENT JOB*
Technician (Electrical)	Laboratory Assistant
Junior Field Engineer	Senior Field Engineer
Engineer	Production Superintendent
Tracer	Application Engineer
Electronic Maintenance Man	Electronic Technician

Transferred to different company

Electrical Technician	Electrical Field Engineer
Engineering Aide	Associate Engineer
Technician (Laboratory)	Associate Engineer
Draftsman	Assistant Engineer
Technician, Electrical	Chief Engineer
Electrician	Electrical Contractor (Self)

16 to 25 years since graduation (Classes of 1932 to 1941)

Remained with same company

Student–Test Course	Design Engineer
Apprentice Electrician	Senior Quality Engineer
Errand Boy	Foreman
Generator & Starter Tester	Tool Engineer
Test Man	Technical Engineer
Assembler–Electric Typewriters	Assistant Plant Superintendent
Electrical Maintenance Man	Electrical Draftsman
Pump Operator	Senior Operator and Foreman
Draftsman	Senior Engineer
Power Plant Office Clerk	Superintendent of Hydro & Distribution Station

Transferred to different company

Design Engineer	Plant Engineer
Lighting Sales Engineer	Southern Sales Mgr.–Light Sales
Blueprint Clerk	Product Design Engineer

* The first job and present job reported in sections B, C, and D are for the same individual in each case. That is, the individual who reported his first job as being an "Assistant Lab Technician" also reported that his present job was "Photographic Engineer."

FIRST JOB*	PRESENT JOB*
Line Layout Man	Asst. Sup't. of Engineering
Tracer	Mgr. Administrative Engineering
Inspector, Electrical	Circuit Designer
Installer	Design Engineer
Relay Inspector	Pres. & Sec'y.–Electrical Store
Draftsman	Senior Engineer

D. *Representative first jobs and 1957 jobs for a group of typical engineering technicians graduated in Mechanical Technology 1927–1956 by Rochester Institute of Technology.*

FIRST JOB*	PRESENT JOB*

6 to 10 years since graduation (Classes of 1947 to 1951)

Remained with same company

Draftsman	Designer–Product Engineering
Process Engineer	Inspection Foreman
Designer	Associate Engineer
Draftsman	Engineer
Detail Draftsman	Development Engineer
Draftsman	Associate Engineer
Detail Draftsman	Test Process Engineer
Handyman	Assistant Engineer

Transferred to different company

Project Engineer	Chief Engineer
Junior Tool Designer	Tool Designer
Junior Tool Designer	Process Engineer
Engineer in Training	Mechanical Engineer
Tool Designer	Senior Tool Designer
Tool Designer	Project Engineer
Apprentice Tool Maker	Tool Engineer

* The first job and present job reported in sections B, C, and D are for the same individual in each case. That is, the individual who reported his first job as being an "Assistant Lab Technician" also reported that his present job was "Photographic Engineer."

FIRST JOB *   SECOND JOB *

16 to 25 years since graduation (Classes of 1932 to 1941)

Remained with same company

Engineer	Group Head Engineering
Junior Mechanic	Superintendent of Planning
Draftsman	Process Engineer
Installer	Superintendent–Purchasing Agent
Detail Draftsman	Senior Camera Designer
Camera Repairman	Service Engineer
Lab Technician	Chief Metallurgist
Production Engineer	Staff Production Engineer

Transferred to different company

Tool Designer	Machine Designer
Tool Designer	Project Engineer
Tool Designer	President & Owner
Draftsman	President
Design Draftsman	Plant Engineer
Mechanic	Design Engineer
Turret Lathe Operator	Foreman–Metal Fabrication
Mechanic's Helper	Chief Tool Engineer
Draftsman	Chief Draftsman
Draftsman	Senior Design Engineer

* The first job and present job reported in sections B, C, and D are for the same individual in each case. That is, the individual who reported his first job as being an "Assistant Lab Technician" also reported that his present job was "Photographic Engineer."

Appendix 7. Technical institute programs accredited by the Engineers' Council for Professional Development—1958 *

Since there has not been developed any generally accepted terminology that permits full identification of a curriculum of technical institute type by its title alone, a brief statement of the aims and scope of each curriculum is given in the listing that follows.

Accreditation denotes that the curriculum has been examined and that it has been found satisfactory for the stated purpose it is designed to serve. Accreditation does not necessarily imply that a curriculum is essentially equivalent in content or purpose to other curriculums bearing the same or similar titles.

Academy of Aeronautics
(La Guardia Field, New York)

Aircraft Design Technology

A resident, full-time, day program requiring 3300 hours during 110 weeks and leading to the award of a certificate of graduation upon successful completion.

Aircraft Maintenance Technology

A resident, part-time, evening program requiring 1716 hours during 176 weeks and leading to the award of a certificate of graduation upon successful completion.

* Reprinted with permission from Engineers' Council for Professional Development, *Technical Institute Programs in the United States, 1958,* New York, 1958, pp. 4–8.

Airframe and Power Plant Technology

A resident, full-time, day program requiring 3300 hours during 110 weeks and leading to the award of a certificate of graduation upon successful completion.

Airplane Design Technology

A resident, part-time, evening program requiring 1716 hours during 176 weeks and leading to the award of a certificate of graduation upon successful completion.

The Aeronautical University
(Chicago)

Aeronautical Engineering Technology

A resident full-time program of instruction requiring six terms during a period of two years and leading to the award of Associate in Aeronautical Engineering degree upon successful completion.

Broome Technical Community College
(Binghamton, New York)

Chemical Technology

A resident, full-time, day, cooperative program requiring 1687 hours during 64 weeks at the College and 1000 hours of cooperative employment in industry during 25 weeks and leading to the degree of Associate in Applied Science.

Electrical Technology

A resident, full-time, day, cooperative program requiring 1687 hours during 64 weeks at the College and 1000 hours of cooperative employment in industry during 25 weeks and leading to the degree of Associate in Applied Science.

Mechanical Technology

A resident, full-time, day, cooperative program requiring 1687 hours during 64 weeks at the College and 1000 hours of cooperative employment in industry during 25 weeks and leading to the degree of Associate in Applied Science.

Capitol Radio Engineering Institute
(Washington, D.C.)

Correspondence Course in Electronic Engineering Technology

A program of home study courses requiring the equivalent of 112 weeks of full-time study to complete and leading to the award of a diploma upon successful completion determined by examination.

Resident Course in Electronic Engineering Technology

A resident full-time or part-time evening program of instruction requiring a minimum of 112 weeks or the equivalent in part-time work and leading to the award of an Associate in Applied Science degree upon successful completion.

Central Technical Institute
(Kansas City, Missouri)

Basic Radio-Television

A resident full-time program of instruction requiring the equivalent of four semesters and leading to the award of a diploma upon successful completion.

Electronics, Radio, and Television Technology

A resident full-time program of instruction requiring the equivalent of six semesters and leading to the award of an associate degree upon successful completion.

Correspondence Course in Master Radio, Television, Electronics Training

A program of home-study courses requiring the equivalent of four semesters plus eight weeks of resident instruction and leading to the award of a diploma upon successful completion determined by examination.

City College of San Francisco
(San Francisco)

Architectural Engineering Technology

A resident, full-time, day program requiring 1712 hours during 68 weeks and leading to a degree of Associate in Arts or Certificate of Completion.

Building and Contracting Technology

A resident, full-time, day program requiring 1568 hours during 68 weeks and leading to a degree of Associate in Arts or Certificate of Completion.

Civil Engineering Technology

A resident, full-time, day program requiring 1856 hours during 68 weeks and leading to a degree of Associate in Arts or Certificate of Completion.

Design Drafting Technology

A resident, full-time, day program requiring 1984 hours during 68 weeks and leading to a degree of Associate in Arts or Certificate of Completion.

Electrical Engineering Technology

A resident, full-time, day program requiring 1808 hours during 68 weeks and leading to a degree of Associate in Arts or Certificate of Completion.

Electronic Engineering Technology

A resident, full-time, day program requiring 1760 hours during 68 weeks and leading to a degree of Associate in Arts or Certificate of Completion.

General Engineering Technology

A resident, full-time day program requiring 1810 hours during 68 weeks and leading to a degree of Associate in Arts or Certificate of Completion.

Mechanical Engineering Technology

A resident, full-time, day program requiring 1856 hours during 68 weeks and leading to a degree of Associate in Arts or Certificate of Completion.

Cogswell Polytechnic Institute
(San Francisco)

Electronics

A resident full-time program of instruction requiring four semesters during a period of two years and leading to the award of an Associate in Engineering degree.

Machine Design

A resident full-time program of instruction requiring four semesters during a period of two years and leading to the award of an Associate in Engineering degree.

Structural Design

A resident full-time program of instruction requiring four semesters during a period of two years and leading to the award of an Associate in Engineering degree.

University of Dayton Technical Institute
(Dayton, Ohio)

Electrical Technology

A resident full-time or part-time evening program of instruction requiring four semesters or the equivalent in part-time work and leading to the award of an Associate in Engineering degree.

Industrial Technology

A resident full-time or part-time evening program of instruction requiring four semesters or the equivalent in part-time work and leading to the award of an Associate in Engineering degree.

Mechanical Technology

A resident full-time or part-time evening program of instruction requiring four semesters or the equivalent in part-time work and leading to the award of an Associate in Engineering degree.

De Vry Technical Institute
(Chicago)

Electronic Technology and Design

A resident full-time program requiring four terms of instruction during a period of two years and leading to the award of a diploma upon successful completion.

Electronic Technical Institute
(Inglewood and San Diego, California)

Electronics

A resident full-time or part-time evening program of instruction requiring sixty-five weeks or the equivalent in part-time work and leading to the degree of Associate of Science upon successful completion.

Embry-Riddle Aeronautical Institute
(Miami, Florida)

Aeronautical Engineering Technology

A resident, full-time, day program requiring 2192 hours during 96 weeks and leading to the degree of Associate of Science.

Franklin Technical Institute
(Boston)

Chemical Technology

A resident full-time program of instruction requiring four semesters and leading to the award of a certificate upon successful completion.

Civil Engineering Technology

A resident full-time program of instruction requiring four semesters and leading to the award of a certificate upon successful completion.

Electrical and Electronic Engineering Technology

A resident full-time program of instruction requiring four semesters and leading to the award of a certificate upon successful completion.

Mechanical Engineering Technology

A resident full-time program of instruction requiring four semesters and leading to the award of a certificate upon successful completion.

Franklin University
(Columbus, Ohio)

Communication Engineering Technology

A resident full-time program of instruction requiring four semesters during a period of two years and leading to the award of an Associate of Science degree upon successful completion.

Houston, University of
College of Technology
(Houston)

Air Conditioning and Refrigeration Technology

A resident full-time program of instruction requiring four semesters and leading to the award of a Certificate of Achievement or an Associate in Science Diploma.

Diesel Electric Technology

A resident full-time program of instruction requiring six semesters and leading to the award of a Certificate of Achievement or an Associate in Science Diploma.

Diesel Technology

A resident full-time program of instruction requiring four semesters and leading to the award of a Certificate of Achievement or an Associate in Science Diploma.

Drafting Technology

A resident full-time program of instruction requiring four semesters and leading to the award of a Certificate of Achievement or an Associate in Science Diploma.

Electrical Technology

A resident full-time program of instruction requiring four semesters and leading to the award of a Certificate of Achievement or an Associate in Science Diploma.

Electronic Technology

A resident full-time program of instruction requiring four semesters and leading to the award of a Certificate of Achievement or an Associate in Science Diploma.

Lain Technical Institute
(Indianapolis and Evansville, Indiana)

Architectural Drafting

A resident full-time or part-time evening program of instruction requiring nine terms during a period of two years or equivalent in part-time work and leading to the award of an Associate of Science Degree upon successful completion.

Industrial Technology

A resident full-time or part-time evening program of instruction requiring nine terms during a period of two years or equivalent in part-time work and leading to the award of an Associate of Science Degree upon successful completion.

Tool and Gauge Design

A resident full-time or part-time evening program of instruction requiring nine terms during a period of two years or equivalent in part-time work and leading to the award of an Associate of Science Degree upon successful completion.

Mohawk Valley Technical Institute
(Utica, New York)

Electrical Technology

A resident full-time cooperative program requiring six quarters of instruction and two quarters of industrial cooperative training over a period of two years and leading to the award of the degree of Associate of Applied Science upon successful completion.

Mechanical Technology

A resident full-time cooperative program requiring six quarters of instruction and two quarters of industrial cooperative training over a period of two years and leading to the award of the degree of Associate of Applied Science upon successful completion.

Milwaukee School of Engineering
(Milwaukee)

Air Conditioning Technician

A resident full-time or part-time day or evening program of instruction in Refrigeration and Air Conditioning requiring six terms during a period of two academic years or equivalent part-time work and leading to the award of an Associate in Applied Science degree.

Electrical Power Technician

A resident full-time or part-time day or evening program of instruction in Electrical Power and Industrial Electronics and requiring six terms during a period of two academic years or equivalent part-time work and leading to the award of an Associate in Applied Science degree.

Electrical Technician

A resident full-time or part-time day or evening program of instruction in Electrical Technology requiring four terms during a period of one calendar year or equivalent part-time work leading to the award of a Certificate in Electrical Technology.

Electronics Communication Technician

A resident full-time or part-time day or evening program of instruction in Communications and Industrial Electronics requiring six terms during a period of two academic years or equivalent part-time work and leading to the award of an Associate in Applied Science degree.

Industrial Technician

A resident full-time or part-time day or evening program of instruction in Metals Fabrication and Industrial Technology requiring six terms during a period of two academic years or equivalent part-time work and leading to the award of an Associate in Applied Science degree.

New York State Agricultural and Technical Institute
(Alfred University, Alfred, N.Y.)

Diesel Technology

A resident full-time program of instruction requiring six terms during a period of two years and leading to the award of an Associate in Applied Science degree.

Electrical Technology, with options in Electric Power and in Electric Communications

A resident full-time program of instruction requiring six terms during a period of two years and leading to the award of an Associate in Applied Science degree.

Heating and Air Conditioning

A resident full-time program of instruction requiring six terms during a period of two years and leading to the award of an Associate in Applied Science degree.

Mechanical Technology

A resident full-time program of instruction requiring six terms during a period of two years and leading to the award of an Associate in Applied Science degree.

New York State Agricultural and Technical Institute
(Canton, New York)

Electrical Technology

A resident full-time program of instruction requiring four semesters and leading to the award of an Associate in Applied Science degree or a certificate of attendance depending upon individual attainment.

Mechanical Technology—Drafting and Design

A resident full-time program of instruction requiring four semesters and leading to the award of an Associate in Applied Science degree or a certificate of attendance depending upon individual attainment.

Mechanical Technology—Heating and Air Conditioning

A resident full-time program of instruction requiring four semesters and leading to the award of an Associate in Applied Science degree or a certificate of attendance depending upon individual attainment.

Northrop Institute of Technology
(Inglewood, California)

Aeronautical Engineering Technology

A resident full-time program of instruction requiring six semesters during a period of two years and leading to the award of a diploma upon successful completion, OR

A resident full-time cooperative program requiring six

semesters of instruction and eighty weeks of industrial cooperative training over a period of about three and one-half years and leading to the award of a diploma upon successful completion.

Aircraft Maintenance Engineering Technology

A resident, full-time program of instruction requiring six semesters during a period of two years and leading to the award of a diploma upon successful completion, OR

A resident full-time cooperative program requiring six semesters of instruction and eighty weeks of industrial cooperative training over a period of about three and one-half years and leading to the award of a diploma upon successful completion.

Ohio College of Applied Science (Ohio Mechanics Institute) (Cincinnati)

Chemical Technology

A resident full-time cooperative program of instruction requiring four semesters at the institute and forty-eight weeks of industrial cooperative training during a period of two years and leading to the award of an Associate of Science degree upon successful completion.

Construction Technology

A resident full-time cooperative program of instruction requiring four semesters at the institute and forty-eight weeks of industrial cooperative training during a period of two years and leading to the award of an Associate of Science degree upon successful completion.

Electrical Engineering Technology

A resident full-time cooperative program of instruction requiring four semesters at the institute and forty-eight weeks of industrial cooperative training during a period of two years and leading to the award of an Associate of Science degree upon successful completion.

Mechanical Engineering Technology

A resident full-time cooperative program of instruction requiring four semesters at the institute and forty-seven weeks of industrial cooperative training during a period of two years and leading to the award of an Associate of Science degree upon successful completion.

Oklahoma Institute of Oklahoma State University
School of Technical Training—A Division of Oklahoma State University
(Stillwater, Oklahoma)

Air Conditioning and Refrigeration

A resident full-time program of instruction requiring four semesters and leading to the award of a technician's certificate upon successful completion.

Building Construction

A resident full-time program of instruction requiring four semesters and leading to the award of a technician's certificate upon successful completion.

Diesel and Stationary Engines

A resident full-time program of instruction requiring four semesters and leading to the award of a technician's certificate upon successful completion.

Drafting and Design

A resident full-time program of instruction requiring four semesters and leading to the award of a technician's certificate upon successful completion.

Electrical Technology

A resident full-time program of instruction requiring four semesters and leading to the award of a technician's certificate upon successful completion.

Fire Protection

A resident full-time program of instruction requiring four semesters and leading to the award of a technician's certificate upon successful completion.

Radio and Electronics

A resident full-time program of instruction requiring four semesters and leading to the award of a technician's certificate upon successful completion.

Oregon Technical Institute
(Klamath Falls, Oregon)

Electronics Technology

A resident, full-time, day program requiring 1896 hours during 66 weeks and leading to a diploma.

Structural Design Technology

A resident full-time day program requiring 1896 hours during 66 weeks and leading to a diploma.

Surveying Technology

A resident full-time day program requiring 1896 hours during 66 weeks and leading to a diploma.

The Pennsylvania State University
Extension Services—Programs offered in extension centers
(University Park, Pennsylvania)

Drafting and Design Technology

An extension center full-time program of instruction requiring four semesters over a period of two years and leading to the award of an Associate in Engineering degree upon successful completion.

Electrical Technology

An extension center full-time program of instruction requiring four semesters over a period of two years and leading to the award of an Associate in Engineering degree upon successful completion.

Purdue University
Division of Technical Institutes—Programs offered in exten-sion centers
(West Lafayette, Indiana)

Building Construction Technology

An extension center full-time or part-time evening pro-gram requiring four semesters during a period of two years or the equivalent part-time work and leading to the award of an Associate Technical Aide diploma upon successful completion.

Drafting and Mechanical Technology

An extension center full-time or part-time evening pro-gram requiring four semesters during a period of two years or the equivalent part-time work and leading to the award of an Associate Technical Aide diploma upon suc-cessful completion.

Electrical Technology

An extension center full-time or part-time evening pro-gram requiring four semesters during a period of two years or the equivalent part-time work and leading to the award of an Associate Technical Aide diploma upon successful completion.

Industrial Technology

An extension center full-time or part-time evening pro-gram requiring four semesters during a period of two years or the equivalent part-time work and leading to the award of an Associate Technical Aide diploma upon successful completion.

RCA Institutes
(New York)

Advanced Electronics

A resident full-time day or part-time evening program of instruction requiring nine terms during a period of twenty-seven months or the equivalent in part-time work and leading to the award of a certificate upon successful completion.

Rochester Institute of Technology
(Rochester, New York)

Electrical Technology

A resident full-time cooperative program of instruction requiring the equivalent of four semesters at the institution and forty weeks of industrial cooperative training and leading to the award of the Degree of Associate in Applied Science.

Industrial Chemistry

A resident full-time cooperative program of instruction requiring the equivalent of four semesters at the institution and forty weeks of industrial cooperative training and leading to the award of the Degree of Associate in Applied Science.

Mechanical Technology

A resident full-time cooperative program of instruction requiring the equivalent of four semesters at the institution and forty weeks of industrial cooperative training and leading to the award of the Degree of Associate in Applied Science.

Photographic Technology

A resident full-time program of instruction in the materials and processes of photography or laboratories requiring chemical and sensitometric control, requiring four semesters and leading to the award of the Degree of Associate in Applied Science.

Sinclair College
(Dayton, Ohio)

Mechanical Engineering Technology

A resident full-time day cooperative or noncooperative program requiring 1408 hours in 48 weeks at the College and (in the cooperative program) 50 to 52 weeks in industry or part-time evening program requiring 1328 hours and leading to a degree of Associate in Engineering Administration.

Tool Engineering Technology

A resident full-time day cooperative or noncooperative program requiring 1504 hours in 48 weeks at the College and (in the cooperative program) 50 to 52 weeks of cooperative training in industry or a part-time evening noncooperative program requiring 1488 hours and leading to a degree of Associate in Engineering Administration.

Southern Technical Institute
A Division of Georgia Institute of Technology
(Chamblee, Georgia)

Building Construction Technology

A resident full-time or part-time evening program of instruction requiring six terms during a period of two years or the equivalent part-time work and leading to the award of an Associate in Science degree.

Civil Technology

A resident full-time or part-time evening program of instruction requiring six terms during a period of two years or the equivalent part-time work and leading to the award of an Associate in Science degree.

Electrical Technology

A resident full-time or part-time evening program of instruction requiring six terms during a period of two years or the equivalent part-time work and leading to the award of an Associate in Science degree.

Electronic and Communications Technology

A resident full-time or part-time evening program of instruction requiring six terms during a period of two years or the equivalent part-time work and leading to the award of an Associate in Science degree.

Gas and Fuel Technology

A resident full-time or part-time evening program of instruction requiring six terms during a period of two years or the equivalent part-time work and leading to the award of an Associate in Science degree.

Heating and Air-Conditioning Technology

A resident full-time or part-time evening program of instruction requiring six terms during a period of two years or the equivalent part-time work and leading to the award of an Associate in Science degree.

Industrial Technology

A resident full-time or part-time evening program of instruction requiring six terms during a period of two years or the equivalent part-time work and leading to the award of an Associate in Science degree.

Mechanical Technology

A resident full-time or part-time evening program of instruction requiring six terms during a period of two years or the equivalent part-time work and leading to the award of an Associate in Science degree.

Spring Garden Institute
(Philadelphia)

Electronic and Electrical Technology

A resident full-time program of instruction requiring five quarters and leading to the award of a diploma upon successful completion.

Mechanical Technology

A resident full-time program of instruction requiring six quarters and leading to the award of a diploma upon successful completion.

State Technical Institute
(Hartford, Connecticut)

Electrical Technology

A resident full-time program of instruction requiring six terms during a period of two years and leading to the award of a diploma upon successful completion.

Mechanical Technology

A resident full-time program of instruction requiring six terms during a period of two years and leading to the award of a diploma upon successful completion.

Tool Technology

A resident full-time program of instruction requiring six terms during a period of two years and leading to the award of a diploma upon successful completion.

Valparaiso Technical Institute
(Valparaiso, Indiana)

Electronic Engineering Technology

A resident full-time day program requiring 2504 hours during 96 weeks and leading to a degree of Associate in Engineering Electronics.

Electronic Technology

A resident full-time day program requiring 1880 hours during 72 weeks and leading to a Certificate in Electronic Technology.

Ward School of Electronics, University of Hartford
(Hartford, Connecticut)

Engineering Aide—Communications

A resident full-time day program requiring 2400 hours during 96 weeks.

Engineering Aide—Industrial Electronics

A resident full-time day program requiring 2400 hours during 96 weeks.

Wentworth Institute
(Boston)

Aircraft Maintenance Technology

A resident full-time day program requiring 2040 hours during 70 weeks and leading to a Certificate of Graduation.

Architectural Engineering Technology

A resident full-time day program requiring 2040 hours during 70 weeks and leading to a degree of Associate in Engineering.

Building Construction Technology

A resident full-time day program requiring 2040 hours during 70 weeks and leading to a Certificate of Graduation.

Electrical Engineering Technology—Electronics Option

A resident full-time day program requiring 2040 hours during 70 weeks and leading to a degree of Associate in Engineering.

Electrical Engineering Technology—Power Option

A resident full-time day program requiring 2040 hours during 70 weeks and leading to a degree of Associate in Engineering.

Mechanical Engineering Technology—Design Option

A resident full-time day program requiring 2040 hours during 70 weeks and leading to a degree of Associate in Engineering.

Mechanical Engineering Technology—Heat Power Option

A resident full-time day program requiring 2040 hours during 70 weeks and leading to a degree of Associate in Engineering.

Mechanical Technology—Design Option

A resident full-time day program requiring 2040 hours during 70 weeks and leading to a Certificate of Graduation.

Mechanical Technology—Machine Processes Option

A resident full-time day program requiring 2040 hours during 70 weeks and leading to a Certificate of Graduation.

Production Engineering Technology

A resident full-time day program requiring 2040 hours during 70 weeks and leading to the degree of Associate in Engineering.

West Virginia Institute of Technology
(Montgomery, West Virginia)

Industrial Electricity

A resident full-time program of instruction requiring four semesters over a period of two years and leading to the award of an Associate in Science degree.

Wyomissing Polytechnic Institute
(Wyomissing, Pennsylvania)

Engineering Technology

A resident full-time cooperative program requiring five periods of instruction at the institute and fifty-five weeks of industrial cooperative training over a period of two-and-a-half years and leading to a Certificate of Graduation.